0311

KU-048-281

Comfrey

by the same author

GROW YOUR OWN FRUIT AND VEGETABLES

DOWN TO EARTH GARDENING

COMFREY
Past, present and future

by

LAWRENCE D. HILLS

FABER AND FABER LIMITED
3 Queen Square London

First published in 1976
by Faber and Faber Limited
3 Queen Square London WC1
Printed in Great Britain by
Ebenezer Baylis and Son Limited
The Trinity Press, Worcester, and London
All rights reserved

ISBN 0 571 11007 x
(Faber Paperbacks)

ISBN 0 571 10521 1
(hard-bound edition)

CONDITIONS OF SALE
This book is sold subject to the condition that it shall not, by way of
trade or otherwise, be lent, re-sold, hired out or otherwise circulated
without the publisher's prior consent in any form of binding or cover
other than that in which it is published and without a similar condition
including this condition being imposed on the subsequent purchaser

© this edition by Lawrence D. Hills 1976

Contents

Illustrations

9

The line drawings for figures 1, 2, 4, 5, 6 and 7 are by David Kenning

Preface

This book is the story of a crop that has grown as fast and deeply into my life as it grows on the land. It began with Henry Doubleday whose dream it was that his crop would feed a hungry world when his vision came from the Irish Potato Famine of the 1840s, and it is mine, for today there are more people to be hungrier, far sooner than we think.

Ever since 1948, when I first grew comfrey, I have had the help of others, especially from members of the Henry Doubleday Research Association which I founded in 1954 and named in honour of the Quaker who introduced the crop. First I would thank the farmers and gardeners who 'rode in the Comfrey Races' of 1955 and 1956, General Sir Philip Christison, L. G. Fairchild, Ian Macdonald and Paul Weir who are still with us, the late Mrs. P. B. Greer, and Vernon Stephenson, who died in January 1974. His thirty-four-year-old plot at Hunsley House Stud has been abandoned to grass and weeds, but his long experience with horses has contributed greatly to this book.

I would like to express my gratitude to Andrew Hughes of Japan for the material in this book relating to that country of 28,000 comfrey growers where he pioneered its cultivation. The world's record for continuous comfrey production is held by 'Phil' Phillips of Rhodesia with an average of a hundred tons an acre for seventeen successive years on his twenty-five-acre field at Mteroshanga, and I thank him for his photographs, his friendships and his generous help over the past twenty years. Thanks are also due to Dr. H. L. Knowles of Davis College, University of California, for permission to use the records of the experiments that grew over the hundred tons an acre for the first time in the U.S.A. I owe more than thanks to Mrs. Beth Setzer of Seattle for her kindness and valued assistance during my visit to the comfrey growers of the United States in 1974 and to Dr. Bargyla Rateaver for the help she has given me.

I am not medically qualified and therefore cannot write on the medicinal uses of comfrey without jeopardizing the possibilities of serious research on this plant that was the first of all the 'wonder drugs' in A.D. 400 when it was described by Discourides. I could fill chapters with reported cures but these would not be acceptable to modern medicine in the same way that my analysis and yield figures should be to agricultural science. I have therefore used as my medical chapter the account by the late Dr. Charles J. Mac-Alister of his work with comfrey. He died in 1941 and his widow gave the copyright of his book to the Association so her husband's work would go on. It has been the basis of our work in this field and it is still our hope that we shall some day have a medical research team working on the development of comfrey. I would like to thank Mrs. MacAlister on behalf of all who have been helped by comfrey, and Dr. A. W. Titherley D.Sc., Ph.D., F.I.C. for Appendix 2 on the chemistry of allantoin. I would also acknowledge the help of Dr. Denys Long, Ph.D. for Appendix 1 on the possible danger of a toxic alkaloid in comfrey, which he exploded with the co-operation of the Medical Research Council. I am grateful to Mr. David Kenning for his excellent line drawings.

My first book on comfrey was published in 1953 and it has been long outdated by new discoveries. Twenty-two years later, this present book is still only an interim report, for the work of the Henry Doubleday Research Association goes on. If you are really interested in comfrey, write to me at the address below—by the time you read this our research may have written another chapter in the story of the crop that is my life.

LAWRENCE D. HILLS

Henry Doubleday Research Association
Bocking
Braintree
Essex   *August 1975*

1. Russian comfrey and its history

Russian comfrey is a perennial fodder crop, in the lucerne class for nutritional value but with a vastly greater yield. This yield, in from six to eight cuts between early April and the end of November, totals forty tons an acre for a poor crop, and a hundred tons for a good one. It is a member of the order *Boraginaceae* and therefore avoids the galaxy of viruses and eelworms that beset so many modern crops. Its high average protein of 24 per cent of the dry matter, and low average fibre at 10 per cent when cut at the leafy stage, makes it ideally suited for pigs and poultry.

'Russian comfrey is a weed: no stock will eat it; its yield in dry matter per acre is below that of orthodox fodder crops; it is impossible to get rid of, and fit only for a half-hearted trial on an odd corner of land where nothing else will grow. Its possibilities have been greatly overrated by those who sell it at high prices, and nothing reliable is known about it. . . .'

For over a hundred and fifty years these opinions in conflict, favourable and unfavourable views, have kept this plant a flying saucer of agriculture, briefly sighted still in the correspondence columns of the farming press. Yet hidden in the recurring controversy lies a crop that could lift the world out of its chronic high-grade protein shortage. Meat, butter, milk, and eggs all demand more space on the land to grow the feed that produces them than do crops for direct human consumption, which are up to eight times as efficient in terms of mouths fed per acre. In Britain we have only one-third of an acre of fertile land for every one of our fifty-three million people, and every year roughly 150,000 'thirds' go under homes, roads, playing fields and factories. It is only by increasing production from the 'thirds' available for crops (and bringing less fertile land into cultivation) that we can continue to eat, especially when countries overseas do not wish to exchange the produce of their acres for the goods we have to offer.

It is the purpose of this book to clear the myth and mystery from a fodder crop whose yield, with good husbandry, far outweighs its disadvantages, for the general farmer, the pig and poultry farmer, the small-holder, and the amateur gardener and poultry-keeper.

The story of Russian comfrey begins in 1771. In this year Joseph Busch, a nurseryman and landscape gardener of Well Street, Hackney, London E.8, sold his business (which now has a London Passenger Transport Board garage on its site) to Conrade Loddige, another rising nurseryman. With the casual internationalism of the slower but freer world of horses and sailing ships, he had taken a job as head gardener to the Palace of St. Petersburg for the Empress Catherine II (the Great) of Russia. From his new job, some time between 1790 and 1801, he sent back several Symphytums as garden plants, relations of the wild *S. officinale*, the Common Comfrey, with which they shared the habit of having thirty-six chromosomes in each cell (see *Chromosomes Atlas of Cultivated Plants* by C. D. Darlington and Dr. E. K. Janaki Ammal, Allen & Unwin).

Messrs. Loddige, now 'and Sons', had expanded greatly, buying from St. Thomas's Hospital the land that is now St. Thomas's Square and Loddiges Road, whose name commemorates this famous nursery. Though they were mainly cashing-in on the great days of British greenhouses with stove plants and orchids (they were importing orchids from Montevideo, Uruguay, in 1812, the year of Napoleon's retreat from Moscow), they grew a wide range of hardy subjects. These included 1,393 different species and hybrid roses and no fewer than seven Symphytums. The 16th edition of their catalogue, dated 1836, is in the Hackney Public Library. Unfortunately this is not descriptive, but like many of the more dignified publications of this time, consists of names only, rather resembling a Kew hand-list.

The seven Symphytums included *S. asperrimum* Donn. (the last word is the abbreviated name of the botanist who first described it) which is illustrated in colour facing page 929 of *Curtis's Botanical Magazine* for 1806. 'This species of the Symphytum, a native of the Caucasus, is by far the largest of the Genus, growing to the height of five feet, an ornamental perennial which will thrive in any soil or situation.' Its flower-stem leaves are always opposite and its leaves and stems are not only hairy but covered with short, stiff bristles, hence its popular name of 'Prickly Comfrey', and its specific one of *asperrimum* or 'the roughest'. Its flowers are vivid blue and both the illustration in Curtis and plate 77 (both in colour) of *The Ladies' Flower Garden* by John Claudius Loudon (vol. 2 of the 1844 edition), show not only its beauty, but the skill of the engraver. When grown uncut it flowers freely and does not produce the weight of foliage that gives it agricultural value, though it must have been on the powerful side in the well-manured herbaceous border. *The Dictionary of Gardening* (Royal Horticultural Society, 1952, 4 vols.) still recommends it as a plant for the wild garden.

Another nurseryman, near Lewisham, was the first to discover the agricultural possibilities of the plant. James Grant, of whose catalogues and history not a trace remains, claimed yields of from forty to sixty tons an acre in from five to six cuts a year. On good land it grew up to seven feet high, but the weight was obtained by constant cutting, using the growth pressure of the great roots, like those of a dock but larger and stronger (for they drive up to eight feet into the ground) to secure growth speed, as the velocity of water is increased by a thumb over the tap. The simile is rough, for the roots were alive and stimulated by the cutting.

The first available reference to James Grant and his crop, which was launched about 1810, is in *The Encyclopaedia of Agriculture*, an earlier work (1825) by John C. Loudon, the Scottish botanist and writer (1782–1843). Since that date much agriculturally cultivated comfrey has been called *Symphytum asperrimum*, though Mr. C. Bucknell in a paper read to the Linnean Society on 19 June, 1913, dealing with the nomenclature of the Symphytums, re-christened Joseph Busch's introduction *S. asperum*, and the R.H.S. *Dictionary* adopts this new name officially. As this book is concerned with agriculture, and not botany or horticulture, the change will be ignored, because the synonym has been used for 150 years and in the circumstances it would cause confusion, for every available reference in farming literature uses the old name.

The plant slowly found its way into the many general works on agriculture published in the middle years of the nineteenth century. David Low's Dictionary of 1836, and Martin Doyle's *A Cyclopaedia of Practical Husbandry* of 1843, both endeavour to identify *S. asperrimum* with the 'Trottel' described by Arthur Young in his *The Farmer's Callender* of 1822. The latter was a mysterious tuberous-rooted vegetable, imported from Labrador and grown by James Sibbald, Esq. of Paisley and a nurseryman at Greenock; but since it turned yellow inside when cooked, while *Symphytum asperrimum* does not, but stays white like a potato and tastes rather like a parsnip, the 'Trottel' (whatever it was) can be safely removed from the confused history of the comfreys.

Perhaps the best early account is found in *The Rural Cyclopaedia, Or a General Dictionary of Agriculture* edited by the Rev. J. M. Wilson (1847), which ran into many editions. He quoted the first cut-by-cut yield figures from Ireland, into which country the crop was introduced by the Bishop of Kildare, and a Dr. Derenzy. The Rev. Henry More, at Carnew Castle in 1835, recorded $28\frac{1}{2}$ tons an acre on 28 April, 31 tons in mid-July, and $22\frac{1}{2}$ tons in mid-September. He recommends planting 15 inches apart and 2 feet between the rows, but gives no details of the spacing or manurial treatment used to secure the Carnew Castle yield. A small hybrid that appeared in 1825 is mentioned as unsuitable for agriculture.

John C. Martin, who edited *A Cyclopaedia of Agriculture* in 1856, states that though our native *Symphytum officinale* was grown as a fodder crop for its succulent shoots produced in early spring, of greater value than the unimproved pre-'early bite' grasses of the time, it was falling into disuse in favour of two exotic species, *S. asperrimum* and *S. echinatum*, which gave heavier yields. However, *Morton's Encyclopaedia of Agriculture*, published about this date in two volumes, described *Symphytum officinale* only, attributing to it the qualities of the Prickly Comfrey, a mistaken attribution taken over by many later writers.

The native species, as its specific name of '*officinale*' or 'of the (Herbalist's) shop' denotes, was of considerable value in medicine.

The earliest description in Turner's *Herball* (1568) includes the following passage: 'The rootes are goode if they be broken and dronken for them that spitte bloode and are bursten, the same layde to are goode to glewe together freshe woundes.'

Fig. 1 The common comfrey is *Symphytum officinale*, known to herbalists for about two thousand years.

Gerard, in his better-known *Herball* first published in 1597, is more detailed in his account 'Of Comfrey or Great Consound', and the following extract is quoted from the 1633 edition in the R.H.S. Lindley Library: 'The Great Comfrey hath rough hairy stalks and long rough leaves much like the garden Buglosse but greater and blacker [darker green], and floures be round and hollow like little bells of a white colour, the roote is black without and white within and very slimey. This differeth in no way from the former [*Symphytum officinale* var. *patens*] but onely in the colour of the floure which is yellowish when the other is reddish or purple ... Comfrey joyeth in watery ditches, in fat and fruiteful meadows, they grow all in my garden. ... The rootes of Comfrey stamped and the juice drunke with wine helpeth those that spit blood and healeth all inward woundes and burstings.'

Master Gerard was prescribing an 0·06 per cent dose of diureide of glyoxyclic acid called 'allantoin' today. This is present in the roots and leaves of both *S. officinale* and *S. asperrimum* and its value as a cell-proliferant in making the edges of wounds grow together, healing sores, and internally for gastric and duodenal ulcers and intestinal irritations causing diarrhoea, is still recognized in pharmacy. A full account is given in *Squire's Companion to the British Pharmacopoeia* (1916) and the recommended strength for external application on lint changed three or four times a day of 0·04 per cent to 0·05 per cent is near enough to the natural 0·06 per cent to 'glewe together freshe woundes' for Master Turner's patients' safety, apart from the risk of bacterial infection.

In the circumstances, with no antiseptics, no anaesthetics, no possibility of successful surgery and with knowledge of the workings of the human body based largely on theory, Master Gerard's prescription, in wine with enough alcohol content to sterilize it, probably gave his patient the best possible chance of surviving an 'internal bursting'. If this were acute appendicitis or peritonitis, the chance would be very slim but, as in Pepys's day when a 'swift colic' was a similar killing disease, the 'bursting' covered a wide range of internal complaints.

The justification for the name 'Symphytum' from the Greek of Dioscorides, *Syumphuo*, best translated 'to make grow together', is found in the pigman's tradition that comfrey cures scour, and the modern comfrey growers' opinion that it prevents and cures intestinal and digestive troubles in pigs, cattle and horses; and it can still be found among the thronging 'mycins' of modern medicine. The most recent reference to allantoin is in the 23rd edition of *The Extra Pharmacopoeia* (Pharmaceutical Press, 1952).

In *Veterinary Pharmacology, Materia Medica and Therapeutics* by Holland J. Milks, D.V.M. (Baillière, Tindall & Cox, 1949), allantoin is described from the standpoint of animal medicine. It is a white crystalline powder which dissolves slowly in cold water but easily in hot, and with thicker skins, external applications can go up to 2 per cent. It can now be made synthetically instead of being extracted by herbalists, from the dried roots or leaves, but is not greatly used, as more effective remedies are known. As it is present in the urine of many animals, it is of importance in some clinical tests. Robinson in 1935 isolated this substance in the excretions of maggots in plaster-cast-treated fractures, explaining why these infestations actually encouraged quicker healing and better knitting of broken bones, especially where osteomyelitis had delayed recovery. That is why this plant that 'joyeth in watery ditches' still numbers 'Knitbone' among its country names. It could naturally set a bone crooked just as easily, but must in the past have saved many limbs with compound fractures or complications.

As Gerard says, we have one other native comfrey, rare except in Scotland, 'with floures of an overworne yellow colour. The rootes are thicke, shorte, black without and tuberous, which, in the figure are not expressed so large and knobbly as they ought to be.' This is *S. tuberosum*, possibly the 'Trottel', which grows only 9 inches to 21 inches high, a smaller plant of no agricultural or medicinal value, with 72 chromosomes—a number which luckily keeps it out of the comfrey confusion. Gerard's warning against his own illustrator is as characteristic of his age as his language. These 'Doctors of Medicine', in the Kipling sense of the term, were far more careful to identify the right plant than many modern herbal writers; they knew that lives depended on their accuracy.

Symphytum officinale with cream, white or yellow flowers, and its variety *S. officinale* var. *patens* with purple, varying in height from one to four feet, will be found pure along the North Downs and in many parts of southern England, but are rarer in the north. Broadly speaking, they have paler green foliage, a higher fibre content, and lesser growth speed; even with increased vigour from good manurial treatment and cultivation, they cannot compare with the imported species.

The flowers of the Symphytums are peculiar in having the stamens covered with a kind of false bottom impassable to honey thieves, made up of five awl-shaped growths that thrust in from the sides of the corolla; but this false bottom can be pushed aside by the humble-bee that alone can fertilize the flower. This device seems at its most obstructive in *S. asperrimum*, and other bees bite a hole in the side of the flower to reach the nectar. The difficulty of the process means that seed is rarely set: *S. officinale* is by far the easiest and produces the most, but even when seed is obtained it is slow to germinate and takes years to produce a crop; so that the agricultural comfreys have always been increased by division or root cuttings.

No other farm crop is propagated vegetatively (grafted fruit trees do not concern the general farm) and the tubers of the potato are about the most costly 'seed' per acre on the farm. Increasing Symphytums by division multiplies them rather less rapidly than Michaelmas daisies, and though plants raised from root cuttings are very much easier and cheaper to produce than oriental poppies, Japanese anemones, and the border phloxes in a nursery, the cost is still high.

Therefore the crop was 'oversold', like 'Soil Conditioners' in the United States in the 1950s, and because the cost of planting an acre was so high (12s. per 100, £5 per 1,000 in 1878 from Sutton's: James Grant's price is unknown) its good qualities had to be magnified in advertising. The very minimum of practical information on cultivation or on overcoming its disadvantages was given, to avoid the impression that it was a complicated crop to grow, for farmers will only tackle complications that they understand. An honest account of the problems and difficulties of making hay would prevent any conservative farmer from tackling the crop, were grass 'new-fangled' and expensive. Comfrey was recommended for every type of soil, and it was claimed that its great yields could be achieved where nothing else would grow, without manuring.

In justification for James Grant and other early nurserymen, it should be said that the knowledge of plant metabolism and soil fertility available at the time was limited. Rothamsted, founded in 1841, was far too preoccupied with measuring the results of artificial fertilizer applications, crop rotations, and the value of legumes; serious agricultural experimenters were too busy trying many exciting applications of new discoveries to have much time for a new crop, sold expensively by nurserymen, and gathering a bad reputation.

The high price meant that only small quantities were bought for trial, and on any farm it is the small odd plot that is most easily ruined by neglect. Comfrey failed from nitrogen starvation on poor soils. Wherever it failed, it remained as a weed, because it is tenacious of life, and struggles on, starved out of all resemblance to the towering fountain of leaves achieved by good husbandry. The high price also accounts for the quite extraordinary number of clergymen in the history of comfrey. The country parson, with his glebe land, his horse, and his Gilbert-White-like interest in Nature and the Useful Arts, was the most frequent buyer.

Finally, both clergy and farmers began to collect *Symphytum officinale* which, as has been observed, will increase its yield with cultivation. This cost less and was largely responsible for the hybrids, with *S. asperrimum* as the pollen parent, which are found in many districts more commonly than the true plant known to Gerard. (See *Handbook of the British Flora* by George Bentham and Sir J. D. Hooker, any edition.)

Attempts were made to secure seed by artificial pollination, but according to Thomas Christy, F.L.S., in his *Forage Crops* (1876), with little success except where the wild Borage, *Borago officinalis*, supplied the pollen. This seed was sold and germinated, but the plants raised 'did not contain the mucilaginous and other properties of the true Caucasian comfrey, and the result is seen in different parts of the country in a variety of comfrey having smaller foliage, paler leaves, and lilac or cream-coloured flowers'. It is just possible that the bi-generic cross came off between the 36-chromosome *Symphytum asperrimum* and the 16-chromosome *Borago officinalis*; after all, the original cross-fertilizations between

species that gave us the ancestors of the modern border iris
I. germanica were made in equal defiance of the then-unknown
laws of genetics. Even as sterile mules the plants would persist as
roots, repropagated constantly by the despairing hoeings and
ploughings of the farmer, perhaps passing on pollen for further
back-crosses with the wild species.

The result of this confusion is seen in letters to (among other
periodicals), the *Gardeners Chronicle*, the earliest from their first
'Constant Reader' in the seventeenth issue of their first volume,
dated 24 April, 1841. These alternate through the 1840s, 1850s
and 1860s with a peak in the seventies and eighties, in a regular
pattern. First a reader inquires about the crop, or gives a glowing
account of it; then others rush in to tell him that it is a weed
and utterly useless. It is referred to variously as *S. asperrimum* and
S. officinale, and even the most enthusiastic give few details of how
it has been grown, or what exactly has been cultivated. The plant
itself is blamed for bad crops and praised for good, very much as
kale would be if no distinction were made between the brassicas
and the wild charlock, with which they share a chromosome
number of 18.

The following extracts are representative of over a hundred of
both types appearing in the *Gardeners Chronicle* then incorporated
with the *Agricultural Gazette*, and other periodicals of this period.

Gardeners Chronicle, 1 February, 1845; 'Cattle will not eat it if
they can get anything better, it must be eaten quite young. The
plant does not deserve the attention it once excited.'

Gardeners Chronicle, 31 March, 1866: '*Symphytum asperrimum*,
the Prickly Comfrey. Some years since we cultivated this to some
extent as a soiling (stall-feeding) crop for cows, and we must say
that these animals will eat it greedily and it seems very useful. Its
crop is large in May and June; when cut down it speedily throws
up a second crop of succulent stems and leaves, but it must be
consumed green as no creature could eat so rough a plant in a dry
state.'

In the 1870s and 1880s comfrey enjoyed a wave of popularity
mainly through the work of four men whose experiments and
writings form part of our basic modern knowledge of the crop.

Fig. 2 The prickly comfrey is *Symphytum asperum*, usually known as
'*Symphytum asperrimum*', and was introduced from Russia between 1790
and 1801.

The most famous of the four was not a comfrey grower; he was Dr.
Auguste Voelcker, D.Sc., F.R.S., Consulting Agricultural
Chemist to the Royal Agricultural Society of England. His article
in the *Journal* of that body (1871, Vol. 7, second series, pages
387–9) entitled 'On the Composition and Nutritive Value of the
Prickly Comfrey (*Symphytum asperrimum*)', gave a very good
account of it, including the Carnew Castle yields. Even more
important, it contains the first analysis ever made of *Symphytum
asperrimum*, from plants grown in Oxfordshire, which he carried
out in 1869. Part of the weight given to this article arose from the

position held by Dr. Voelcker, which involved his testing on behalf of members of the Society samples of concentrated feeding stuffs, 'portable manures' such as Peruvian guano, and mixtures endeavouring to cash in on the new artificial fertilizer market. Many of these commodities were valueless, often fraudulent, and in issues of the *Journal* and by letter, the doctor exposed fraud to the pitiless technique of chemical analysis. Comfrey, however, was not condemned by the verdict.

The general analysis, stems and leaves together, was as follows:

	In natural state	*Calculated dry*
Water	90·66	
Nitrogenous organic compounds (flesh-forming matter)	2·72	29·12
Non-nitrogenous compounds (heat- and fat-producing matter)	4·78	51·28
Mineral matter (ash)	1·84	19·60
	100·00	100·00

Dr. Voelcker stated that 'the juice of this plant is very mucilaginous, though it contains but little sugar . . . notwithstanding the large amount of water the proportion of albuminous compounds (flesh-forming matters) in Comfrey is considerable, and the percentage of cellular fibre is not larger than in similar green food.

'In comparison with other similar food, I may state that Comfrey has about the same feeding value as green mustard, or mangold or turnip tops, or Italian ryegrass grown on irrigated land.'

The last sentence has been quoted for the past eighty years in books on forage crops, and the analysis frequently appears, complete with remarks on albuminous, mucilaginous and flesh-forming matters. These were the proteins, which are complex gummy substances, and of those gelatin was the first to be isolated, with albumen, in white of egg and fish, soon to follow. Gelatin was not then known to be indigestible; the measurement of digestibility was a further refinement of technique, and from this beginning, the custom of giving jellies as invalid food, and testing the quality of a soup from its forming a jelly when cold, survive as errors from these early days.

An even more valuable analysis was supplied to Messrs. Hurst & Sons, the farm and wholesale seedsmen, by Dr. Voelcker, and was fortunately preserved in their records which escaped the East End Blitz of 1940. It is also quoted in *A Modern Herball* by M. Grieve (Jonathan Cape, 1931).

| | LEAVES | | STEMS | |
	Percentage in natural state	Percentage Calculated dry	Percentage in natural state	Percentage Calculated dry
Water	88·40		94·74	
Flesh-forming substances	2·71	23·37	0·69	13·06
Non-nitrogenized substances, heat- and fat-forming	6·90	59·49	3·81	72·49
Inorganic matters (ash)	1·99	17·14	0·76	14·45
	100·00	100·00	100·00	100·00

This is the only analysis we have in which the leaves and stems were treated separately; and they reveal what is common knowledge in these days of ley farming and grassland research, that the best nutritional harvest is in the leaf. Wide variations in comfrey analysis depend on the stage and quality of the cut; there is less water and more protein to lower fibre in a crop cut at the leafy stage, as well as more total weight each season, than where it is allowed to run to stem and flower: a fact which also affects palatability.

The first analysis confirmed what has never been doubted since, the high nutritive value of comfrey. What has been doubted, not to put this more strongly, is its yield. Unlike grain or roots—or even hay or straw which are weighed if sold off the farm—a fodder crop eaten by one's own stock is rarely measured. This type of measurement is made only by research stations and farm institutes, which have very rarely carried out any work on the crop, so that figures are quoted from textbook to textbook. In general, estimates before the 1870s give from 40 to 60 tons an acre; the greater the number of cuts quoted, the higher the estimated yield, with the Rev. Henry More's as the record.

From 1875 onwards we come to 100 ton an acre yields. They

spring from Henry Doubleday (1813–1902) of Coggeshall, Essex, whose ancestors sailed with William Penn to Pennsylvania and founded Messrs. Doubleday & Company Inc., the American publishers. His cousin was Henry Doubleday of Epping, the famous entomologist who compiled the first catalogue of the British Lepidoptera, and his brother Edward was Curator of the Botanical Department of the British Museum.

His father was a grocer—Quakers being barred from the professions by their religious refusal to take an oath—and Henry himself was a great experimenter but a very poor business man. In the 1840s, stirred by the tremendous efforts that were being made to save something from the stinking harvest of blighted potatoes in the Irish Potato Famine, he started a starch factory in Colchester which failed because of a dishonest manager. He then patented a glue which was used by Messrs. de la Rue on the backs of the early postage stamps.

Penny Blacks had originally to be snipped off the sheets with the customer's scissors, and gummed on the letters with his own gum. Later a kind of lickable paste was tried, and then there were many attempts at a gum which did not need a bottle and brush. Henry's blend of glue and gum arabic had the quality of remaining unsticky while sheets of the lovely early Colonials, with Victoria as a young Queen on them, went sailing round the Empire through the humid tropics.

Unfortunately, supplies of gum arabic were erratic, so when Henry, who was a Member of the Royal Agricultural Society of England, saw Dr. Voelcker's article on pages 387–9 of the *Journal* in 1871 he jumped at the word 'mucilaginous'. Here was a crop that would grow gum in Coggeshall. He wrote away to 'The Head Gardener, Palace of St. Petersburg, St. Petersburg, Russia', and his letter arrived safely, for the International Postal Union had been founded in 1863. Joseph Busch had been dead for many years and is still remembered by a most magnificent plan of the grounds he laid out, gardens that are now the Park of Rest and Culture in Leningrad. The tradition by Catherine II of employing English or Scottish head gardeners was still in operation in 1871, and so Henry got his plants.

Joseph Busch had made a border of Symphytums, and had planted the clear sky-blue flowered *S. asperrimum* from the Caucasus, next to the cream-yellow *S. officinale* which not only grows wild in Britain but all over Europe where its popular names in many languages ring the changes on 'Knitbone', 'Wound heal' and 'Sore cure'. It made a fine colour contrast.

When Henry's letter arrived, the then head gardener was not going to break up his large specimens of these long-lived perennials, but dug up some chance seedlings between the rows. It is only very rarely that these two species cross, but it did happen in Sweden and the result was named *S. uplandicum*: what Henry got by train and mail steamer was a parcel of F_1 hybrids, with the hybrid vigour that was first observed in maize and is now familiar in seed catalogues for varieties bred by crossing two pure lines.

Henry had leased some land south of Coggeshall water mill, near the ruins of Coggeshall Abbey where the Cistercian monks began the seed growing that is still a main industry in this village, where they thresh their sweet pea seed with flails, as the best tools for the job. It was here that he tried to breed a blight resistant potato, which he called Berkshire Kidney, but it failed, so he sold his stock to Messrs. Suttons of Reading, and it was here that he planted out his new comfrey.

From his seedlings he selected 'Doubleday's Solid Stemmed Comfrey' and he gives the following record from fifty-four plants on a square rod of ground:

1st Cut, 30 April. In lb. each plant. Total, 1 cwt. 108 lbs. 10, 7¼, 7¼, 5¼, 5¼, 6, 4, 5, 6, 6, 6, 4½, 5¾, 5, 3¾, 4¼, 2¾, 3, 2¾, 3½, 3½, 5, 3½, 4, 3½, 2, 7¼, 3¼, 5¼, 4, 4, 3, 3½, 3, 3¼, 3, 2¼, 2½, 3¼, 4½, 4½, 7, 4½, 2½, 3, 2¼, 2½, 2, 1¾, 2½, 1¾, 2½, 1¾, 1¾, 2, 1¾.
Average per plant 3·93 lb.

Second Cut, 16 June. In lb. per plant. Total 2 cwt. 8¾ lbs.
10½, 3½, 2½, 5¾, 5¾, 1½, 7½, 5½, 5½, 3½, 3, 4½, 2, 4¾, 2¾, 2¾, 11½, 5¾, 6¾, 1½, 2, 5¾, 4¾, 5½, 3, 2½, 2¼, 1¾, 3¼, 5¾, 6¾, 1¼, 2, 5¼, 1, 3¼, 2½, 4¾, 3, 5, 3¾, 2½, 2½, 9, 4, 3¼, 2¼, 5½, 4½, 6, 6, 6½, 8¾.
Average per plant 4·39 lb.

For the two cuts this gives an equivalent yield of 32 tons 6 cwt.

an acre; Henry Doubleday took six cuts and though he did not weigh each cut on this plot, his yield again multiplied by three shows 96 tons 18 cwt. for second-year plants, of a crop that is not at maximum production until the third year. His 10 lb. plant was 4 feet high and 4 feet in diameter, and the illustration opposite shows a similar plant of the same weight grown by the author in 1950. Sixteen pounds is about the record cut for one on a farm, but the aim should be to maintain a high average for the whole season.

On a research station the outer rows and end plants would have been disregarded as 'guards' because these often vary beyond the average (in this case both the 10 lb. plant and a 1¾ lb. one are in these positions) and the weighings continued through the season for every cut. Henry cut approximately 160 lb. per day for his three cows and his pony, and measuring even the yield off a square perch (or square rod or square pole) gives us better evidence than is offered for the low yields often claimed. He grew his strain for many years, and in his letters to the papers including the *Gardeners' Chronicle* (24 October, 1885) stated that he obtained from 100 to 120 tons an acre, in from six to eight cuts.

No one since Henry has secured 100 tons an acre in Britain because no one but the Abbé Gregor Johann Mendel (1822–1884) then knew what happens when you self- or cross-pollinate an F_1 hybrid and no one would believe Mendel, for it was not till sixteen or twenty years after his death that the work of de Vries and Bateson established his discovery of Mendel's Law and taught the world the facts of life and inheritance. Had Henry Doubleday known what we know now, Doubleday comfrey would still be propagated vegetatively as what is called a 'clone', like the scarlet geranium raised by Paul Crampel, the French nurseryman, who pinched out the buds of his plants every night for two years, so that no one would see the splendid colour before the massed display at a Paris Exhibition that brought him a fortune and fame that still lives.

Henry's comfrey is the plant illustrated in plate 6466 of *Curtis's Botanical Magazine* for 1879, for it is stated to be drawn and coloured from the plants presented to Kew by Thomas Christy in 1875. He was a writer, a botanist and a nurseryman living at

Sydenham, who was a Fellow of the Linnean Society and a great friend of Henry Doubleday from whom he obtained comfrey plants. Between them they began the boom in what they called 'Russian Comfrey' to distinguish it from the earlier 'Prickly Comfrey', which was Joseph Busch's *Symphytum asperrimum*. Russian comfrey grew up to 6 feet 8 inches when allowed to run to flower. These flowers were at first blue changing to magenta,

Fig. 3 The Russian comfrey, *Symphytum peregrinum*, introduced by Henry Doubleday in the 1870s, was, so far as we know, a first cross hybrid between the common and prickly comfreys.

and there is a brief account of it in the Kew *Annual Report* for 1878, from which the following is an extract:

'In England it has been found very useful for winter fodder, as it forms large tufts of root leaves which start into growth early in the year and bear several cuttings. It is greedily eaten by animals which refuse ordinary Comfrey, the habit and appearance of which is not very dissimilar.'

In *Curtis's Botanical Magazine*, it is called *Symphytum peregrinum* Ledeb., for it was regarded as the species described by Karl von Ledebour (1785–1851), an Estonian botanist, from specimens he collected 4,000 feet above sea level in the Caucasus. The R.H.S. *Dictionary of Gardening* now agrees that *S. uplandicum* may be the correct name, and to anyone who has grown comfrey, the fact that the rarely set seed produces mixed seedlings, instead of breeding true like all species, is clear proof that *S. peregrinum* was and is a hybrid. I shall continue however to refer to the cultivated comfrey(s) as '*S. peregrinum*', for every botanical authority agrees that 'the nomenclature of the Symphytums is confused' and I have no wish to add further confusion for those who look it up in reference works. It is better to call it 'Comfrey', just as we can refer to seventeen different kales, which are all hybrids of *Brassica olearacea acephala* and *B. oleracea*, known to farmers and gardeners by popular or cultivar names that do not involve botany at all.

It was Thomas Christy who did the selling and wrote the book that put Russian comfrey on the agricultural map with his *Forage Crops* (1877); 'the Solid Stem variety is far more palatable, and in every way they have proved superior to anything grown in this country as Prickly comfrey. On good land, Russian comfrey is fully equal to giving 120 to 150 tons an acre from plants placed one yard apart each way.' This book, illustrated with a rather badly coloured frontispiece of an obvious *S. peregrinum*, had great influence on the cultivation of the crop, which he reinforced in his later works, *New Commercial Plants* in 1878, and *Ensilage* in 1883.

Henry (typically) did not write such privately printed pamphlets which sold at quite good prices as well as helping sales. He wrote letters to the *Gardeners Chronicle* which earned nothing, and spent the last thirty years of his life engaged in research on the crop that it was his dream would feed a hungry world, when this vision came not from Sir John Boyd Orr, or Paul Ehrlich, but the Irish potato famine. Unlike so many of his contemporaries, Henry had a non-commercial mind and he had thought and read his way through the only famine so far in the world's history in which a million *white* people have died.

The last man alive who knew Doubleday was his nephew Thomas, who died in 1957 aged 93. He remembered his dreamy bachelor uncle who took him birds' nesting and talked of his two guiding principles, 'Observe the works of God in humbleness', insisting that by 'humbleness' he meant never allowing yourself to assume that a theory is right because it is your own, and 'Search always for the Truth that harms no man'. The only portrait we have of him was taken at the Great Exhibition in 1851, where for a design of Nottingham lace he won a bronze medal and a statuette of Prince Albert, for lace making was also a Coggeshall industry. It was taken by the Daguerreotype process which involved sitting still for nearly half an hour, which explains the set look on his face.

Henry Doubleday lost the contract with Messrs. de la Rue, when his comfrey protein failed to stick stamps, and the gum business dwindled and died. His smallholding and his share of Thomas Christy's profits supported him modestly, while he worked steadily away finding out all he could about his crop, for which (as his nephew remembered) he bought in stock so that they could be fattened on it, and then failed to drive a hard enough bargain when he sold the animals. He made himself unpopular in the village by opposing the South African Wars, and the last memory of him we have is of a tall thin figure in an old fashioned black overcoat walking up the Tilkey Road from what is now a block of shops called 'Doubleday's Corner', to the Quaker burial ground where more and more of his friends lay as he outlived them. Thomas remembered the village children running after him to ask the time, because he would stop and take out a gold repeater watch that chimed the nearest hour for their delight. It is a family tradition that he was offered a Fellowship of the Royal Society for his introduction of comfrey, but at that time you had to pay a subscription of six guineas on election, and he was too poor to afford the money.

When he died his relations tidied up after him, and all the records of his work were burnt. It is because I was determined that the work I began on comfrey in 1948 should not be destroyed that I founded the Henry Doubleday Research Association in 1954, and named it in the honour of this Quaker, who died poor but whose principles are still our guides however far away from comfrey our work may lead us. The touchstone for whether or not a project of research should be developed by this Association of amateur experimenters in many countries is still 'Would Henry Doubleday, the Friend of agriculture, have thought it a worthy project?'

Apart from Henry and Thomas Christy, there were many keen comfrey growers in the 1870s, and one of the keenest was Kinard B. Edwards of Burbage Hall, Hinckley, Leicestershire. He was perhaps the first of all the writers of little books designed to help the townsman turned countryman. These were published at sixpence (2½p) each and privately printed, so most have vanished; there are none in the British Museum but there is one in the Bodleian Library, Oxford.

In his *An Acre of Land and How to Make the Most of It* (1873) he gives clear directions for the cultivation of the plant as a 'soiling crop' for stall-fed cows, stressing the importance of keeping the land clean and well manured and with adequate cutting. He gives yields of 10 to 15 tons per acre per cut; totals of 50 tons the first year, 80 the second and after that 100 to 120 tons. For the other crops mentioned in this work, yields such as 40 tons an acre for mangolds are normal on good land today. In his *The Amateur's and Cottager's Cow*, date about 1875, he quotes a neighbour of his who has fed three cows and two horses off the produce of a quarter of an acre of comfrey, and gives a normal annual yield of 80 to 90 tons.

Several seedsmen took up the distribution of the plant, and some endeavoured to get over the problem of cost by selling small root cuttings cheaply, but their slow rate of growth the first year, and the handicap of weed competition at this stage, produced very poor results. An illustration from the catalogue of Messrs. Suttons of Reading for 1878, probably *Symphytum peregrinum*, gave a far better idea of how the plant should look on the farm than a botanical drawing showing the flower stem, which is like illustrating celery or sugar-beet with their 'bolters'.

'This forage plant, introduced into this country a few years since, is rapidly increasing in favour. Although we do not agree with all that has been said in its praise, yet we believe it to be a valuable plant for giving a supply of green food in hot dry seasons. The long roots, which penetrate a great distance into the ground, enable it to obtain moisture beyond the reach of ordinary plants. It will succeed in almost any soil but is especially valuable when cultivated on soils of a dry and sandy nature. It is very hardy and gives an early cutting, supplies a constant succession of green food, and, when once planted, is permanent. It is much relished by all kinds of stock, either cut up and mixed with chaff or separately. For milch cows it is most valuable and it is much relished by domestic poultry. It is cultivated by dividing the roots and spring and autumn are the best seasons for planting. Holes should be dug 24 to 30 inches apart each way and filled with well-rotted stable dung. The cuttings should then be deposited and covered over with earth, leaving the crowns $1\frac{1}{2}$ to 2 inches under ground. It is very important to keep the ground clean and free from weeds. When the leaves have grown from 18 to 24 inches high, they should be cut and given to the stock in a fresh green condition. In about six weeks, a second cutting will be ready and a succession of cuttings can be obtained through the summer and autumn. As many as five heavy cuttings, each 20 tons per acre, or 100 tons per acre in one season, have been obtained by good management. If it is cultivated for one or two heavy cuttings, the stems should be allowed to grow to 4 or 5 feet and it may be cut with an ordinary hook, tied up in bundles and conveyed to the homestead as required. We recommend it especially for small occupations, as few crops can be more easily grown or prove so useful to those whose livestock consists of a horse, cow, and a few pigs.'

The Rev. E. Highton of Bude bought 200 plants from Messrs. Suttons in 1875 (they sold it between 1875 and 1896), carried out the 'directions on the packet' to the letter, and cut at the rate of 60 tons an acre the year of planting. He then dug his plants up and kept increasing them till he had a quarter of an acre, maintaining his yield all the time. He reports that house cows and pigs throve on it; by feeding it *ad lib.* to his horses, he reduced the oats ration from 6 to 3 quarts a day without loss of condition.

His report appears in the article on 'Green and Fodder Crops not Commonly Grown that Have Been Found Suitable for Stall Feeding' by Joseph Darby (*Journal of the Royal Agricultural Society of England*, Vol. 18, 1882) which includes a large selection of letters of opinion on the crop, including Henry Doubleday's statement that it yields 120 tons an acre for four to five cuts a season, and lasts twenty years if the land is kept clean and occasionally stirred. T. R. Hulbert, Esq., of North Cerney regarded it as a delusion; 'it needs very good land, plenty of dung and attention, and no stock will eat it if they can get other food.' A Mr. Sewell-Read considered the plants tiresome to cut, costly to collect and expensive to buy. Both Sir Thomas Acland and Lord Morden considered it a useful crop, and the Rev. F. Gilbert White (of Ashburton, not Selborne) considered it splendid fed chaffed with hay, and producing very high-quality butter. It did not taint or cause hove (bloat). No correspondent gave any flower colour, and most are too brief and optimistic (or pessimistic) to give details of how it was grown. In the many articles of this nature which appeared at this period it will be noted that those who grazed it, as distinct from feeding it wilted (as Christy and Doubleday recommend), refer to 'no stock eating it'; those who take three cuts a year give yields in the 40 to 50 ton region; those who cut most often have both the highest yields and opinions of the plant. David Wemyss of Newton Bank, St. Andrews, in 'The Cultivation of Prickly Comfrey and its Uses as a Fodder Plant' (*Transactions of the Highland and Agricultural Society of Scotland*, Vol. XIV, 1882) refers to the 'even better Solid-Stemmed Variety' and gives a yield of 100 to 120 tons of good fodder per acre per annum. He recommends feeding wilted until the stock are used to it, and cutting when half-grown; the plant should never be allowed to become hard and woody. He also stresses the richness of the butter.

The Gardeners Chronicle, The Country Gentleman's Magazine, The Field, The Times, and the journals of all the agricultural societies printed a steady stream of letters, but not so much because of the interest among farmers. The development of 'portable manures' (artificial fertilizers), knowledge of crop rotations and the action of legumes, and the increasing agricultural depression were quite enough to swallow, without a new crop that was also expensive. The plant, as always, interested the letter-writing classes. It was about this time that the most frequently quoted letter of all appeared in an Irish newspaper, stating that no beasts or sheep would eat comfrey, detailing the ploughing, harrowing, hoeing, and finally picking up by hand into baskets unsuccessfully employed, and finished with the plea 'Can you or any of your correspondents tell me how to get rid of it?'

Another problem of the crop was that while it provided a great bulk of fodder in spring and autumn, it was no help in the winter. Its bristly leaves were thought unsuitable for hay, and its thick stems hard to dry except in perfect weather. Thomas Christy's *Ensilage* on the new process advocated it strongly, and so did the following letter in *The Times* for 24 October, 1882, from J. Bailey Denton, a famous authority on agriculture: 'Permit me to draw attention to this omission and thus indirectly to a valuable foreign forage plant (*Symphytum asperrimum*) which affords four to five cuts a year, weighing as much in the aggregate as 100 tons an acre, which appears especially suited for the silo. In fact the extraordinary bulk of cattle food which may be gathered from it, would suggest its special growth as an ingredient of ensilage.'

Unfortunately, the methods of silage-making then known were particularly unsuited to comfrey, a high protein and moisture crop, relatively low in carbohydrates. To quote Professor Stephen J. Watson's *Silage* (Crosby Lockwood & Son, 1951): 'Then in 1885, George Fry published his book, *Sweet Ensilage*, and this, more than anything else, sounded the death knell of silage for the time being, and the process was set back fifty years.' This process

involved rapid heating, and like those used earlier did not intro-
duce molasses. A crop which is naturally high in carbohydrates had
the best chance of producing sufficient lactic acid to arrest decay
by acidity; one higher in protein swamps this effect with the
evil-smelling and complex by-products of their decay. Russian and
Prickly comfrey were the worst possible subjects for bad silage
methods, and it is to this period that all reports of the poor quality
and unpalatability of silage made from the crop can be traced.

From this period comfrey growing fell into decay. The 'Farmer's
Notebooks', the 'Manuals', the 'Encyclopaedias' ran on by
quotation, but with fields falling out of cultivation and agricultural
depression, Russian comfrey began to vanish. The famous plot at
Carnew Castle with age and neglect died out into weeds that can
still be found in the hedgerows. The cost of new planting became
prohibitive with falling prices for farm produce, and new topics
filled the correspondence columns.

In 1900 Messrs. Websters' Nurseries of Stock, Essex, imported
a fresh supply of comfrey from Russia and continued to sell it
through small advertisements in the farming press as the 'James
Grants' of the twentieth century until about 1960. Their stock was
a mixture of variations, mainly solid stemmed and with flowers
ranging from magenta pink to purple and yellow. The writings of
Thomas Christy and Henry Doubleday, with those who copied
them, had given prestige to the name 'Russian Comfrey' and
therefore this name was used to sell whatever was being sold, with
yield figures from the 1870s and 1880s.

The last full and favourable account giving a yield of 80 tons an
acre is in *The Complete Grazier* by William Fream, published in
1900, but it is missing from his more famous *Elements of Agriculture*. A hay analysis was made some time before the 1914–18 War,
for it appears in *The Agricultural Notebook* by Primrose McConnel
(1916) which shows 18·5 per cent crude protein against 13 per cent
for the best meadow hay. The main progress from then until the
1940s was the slow banishment of books to higher and higher
shelves and the salvage campaigns of two wars made the knowledge
and legends of the past still harder to find.

The dead hand of archaeology began to close, and the *Symphy-*

tums become a pigman's legendary cure for scour, a gipsy herbal remedy and an interesting piece of 'country lore'; a myth and a mystery, with a hundred tons an acre of high-protein fodder hidden in its heart.

2. The modern comfrey growers

The first of the modern comfrey growers was the late J. Kenneth Crawley, of Lockerbie, Dumfriesshire. His interest began in 1938 when he planted a small area on the twenty-acre holding to which he retired, after a life spent as a land agent, in 1936. He carried out a number of experiments with the plant, feeding it mainly to cattle, sheep and pigs, but unfortunately the full records he kept were destroyed after his death in November 1943, a great and double loss to the cultivation of *Symphytum peregrinum* in this country.

His first article, 'Prickly Comfrey—A Neglected Fodder Crop', in the *Scottish Farmer* for 28 February, 1942, was followed by one entitled 'Prickly Comfrey' in the *Journal of the Land Agents' Society* for April 1942. In these articles he gives the result of an extensive search of the old accounts, all that he had been able to discover concerning feeding the plant to stock, and a cut-by-cut analysis of his first year yield from 2,250 May-planted offsets of *Symphytum peregrinum* from the Webster strain.

	Moisture per cent	*Crude Protein* per cent	*Fibre* per cent
June cut	86·50	19·22	—
4 June cut	86·90	25·10	11·60
24 July cut	90·03	25·77	8·48
23 August cut	87·09	24·00	9·70
25 September cut	85·06	25·37	8·70
14 October cut	90·30	26·25	11·20
18 November cut	—	25·50	9·18

(Protein and fibre figures on a dry matter basis)

As a result of these articles he was snowed under with letters and requests for plants from all over the country, and he divided and redivided his crop to fill the demand, in aid of the local Nursing Association. He was, however, not interested in sales so much as in vindicating a crop from the past with great possibilities of helping in the war-time stock-feed shortage, and in experiments to find the best ways of feeding it and conserving it for the winter. Very many of his practical discoveries, from his writings and the memories of his farm workers, are incorporated in the present book, and he can perhaps be described as the father of modern comfrey growing. No yield figures remain, but the 70-yard long and 15-yard wide patch, kept undivided for pig food, which was crossed four times a season, is estimated by his foreman to have produced between 45 and 60 tons an acre each year on a very poor soil.

In 1943 he was immensely concerned with the botanical problem and corresponded at length with his friend, Professor K. W. Braid of the Botany Department of the West of Scotland Agricultural College and other authorities, on the confusion of hybrids and species. He intended to write an article on the whole question, which his death, at the age of 70, prevented. He was the first man to insist that the comfreys were genetically mixed, and that to damn the good crops on the evidence of entirely different plants is fundamentally unsound. The yield figures he quoted were from Henry Doubleday, who grew the same plant, but on a good Essex clay, and the two men, separated in time, had much in common. Agriculture owes a great deal to these small men with education, ideas and keenness for research—orthodoxy may, at low levels, scorn the man 'with a bee in his bonnet', but quite often this turns out to be a worker bee.

One of Mr. Crawley's many friends was the late Mr. E. V. Stephenson, a well-known racing-stud owner of Little Weighton, near Hull, and about 1942, what was a unique comfrey patch was planted, with offsets of *Symphytum peregrinum*. This was a tree-shaded three-quarters of an acre, the former site of two old cottages on a poor and very stony Yorkshire limestone soil, near the stable yard and farm buildings and convenient for cutting. Entirely by accident (some chickens escaped and were lost among the great leaves for some days), Mr. Stephenson discovered his simple weeding system. Fowls of any age will not touch comfrey when it is stiff and growing, they eat only the weeds between the rows, and though Henry Doubleday observed in one of his letters to the *Gardeners Chronicle* that pheasants did exactly this, no one had ever hit on this solution to the weed difficulty before. This plot, with a semi-intensive poultry flock on it, was the only one that had been kept clean and cut for a long period, and therefore its owner was completely satisfied with it.

No yields records were kept, it was crossed in daily cuts between five and seven times a year according to fodder needs, the rations being cut by hand and fed as required. Apart from an occasional stirring with a horse hoe, and manuring in the spring, no further labour was expended on this crop, which was growing where only nettles grew before, the rubbish corner to be found on almost every farm in Britain. Approximate weights per season, judged roughly by the daily cuts, give between 30 and 40 tons an acre today.

At first it was used for poultry, calves and pigs, some of it being fed to horses, but its success in improving the condition and curing and preventing scour in mares and foals, as well as young pigs, has resulted in the main crop being reserved for the blood stock. It was fed daily to the stallions, and to all horses brought into the loose boxes as 'off colour' or mares foaling, as part of the standard diet.

The leaves of *Symphytum officinale* and its hybrids, or abandoned escapes of the fodder comfreys, have been fed as a tradition by gipsy horse copers to bring their wares into condition before a fair. This supplementary diet puts the gloss of health on the coat even of a beast doctored by methods with less veterinary and nutritional justification. Fed to about £200,000 worth of racehorses a year, *Symphytum peregrinum* merits Mr. Stephenson's high opinion of it as part of the diet for thoroughbreds.

Mr. Stephenson attempted to establish plants in his stallion paddock so that it could be grazed, but the result was a heavy fall in yield and the comfrey merely struggled along as a weed; an experiment that is still tried again and again. *It is only a crop when it is kept clean, cut and manured*, and at Hunsley House stud it had only poultry manure, for the horse manure sold at a high price to mushroom growers, but comfrey will take crude poultry droppings straight from the battery, though deep litter is more easily handled.

In the autumn of 1948 I saw my first comfrey plant. It was the steel engraving from Suttons' Farm Seeds catalogue, which I have mentioned on page 33, that illustrated a single sheet advertising Russian comfrey from Messrs. Websters, and my uncle, the late Gordon Saunders, of John D. Wood the estate agents, showed it to me. From that day to this I have never lived further away from a comfrey plant than a hundred feet and more than any woman has, this crop has changed my life.

'He's rather a naughty old man,' said my uncle, 'he's given the analysis of marrowstem kale on a fresh weight basis and his Russian comfrey on a dry matter one, so it looks about eight times more protein, but suppose it really *does* grow a hundred tons an acre.' So we added fifty of Mr. Webster's plants to the special German peppermint, the experimental food crops I was to grow for my uncle's grass drier on the Wissington estates, as well as blight-free celery seed and a million celery plants on five acres of high land at Southery in Norfolk.

In 1950 we had plants enough to send several cuts down to the grass drier from a yield at the rate of about 45 tons an acre, and we fed some to pigs and some to cattle, which left a pedigree ley of Aberystwyth grasses and clovers to eat cut comfrey spread on their pasture. The cut comfrey was left to wilt overnight and put through a Robust shredder which solved the problem of the inch-thick stems and thick leaf midribs, before the drying process. The following table shows the results:

Dried matter	Protein per cent	Fibre per cent	Ash per cent	Oil per cent	Carbo- hydrate per cent
Russian comfrey	21·80	14·0	13·60	2·10	37·40
Grass meal (good)	20·3	14·0	8·0	5·8	41·9
Grass meal (poor)	12·1	22·4	9·0	2·2	42·3

Grass meal was then sold on the protein content, and all the comfrey we produced was dried and mixed in with the poor samples to bring the protein up to a better level, especially when the quality fell in the autumn and the demand for a high protein low fibre pig and poultrymeal was at its highest. The meal could not be sold on its own for the shredding made it turn dark brown, and the market liked a green grass meal. Protein shortage has come again to British farms, with soaring soya and fishmeal prices, and though drying fuel costs are up, this process that saved so much imported feed in the 1939–45 War and afterwards could well be revived.

We planted a long strip to mow with a Ferguson with a grass-mower and swathe-board beside and a buck rake to pick up the cut on return loads, and this went on producing about 50 tons an acre each season for many years after I left Southery in 1951 with a breakdown in health. Before I left, however, I had started a trade in comfrey plants that began what is now known as 'Bocking Mixture' and is the 'Quaker Comfrey' of Canada. I did not then know that comfrey was a hybrid. It looked to me a variable species, and like any nurseryman, I propagated the best.

Then I not only wrote of comfrey among the many gardening and farming articles that earned my living, I met Vernon Stephenson and so began the long chase through the libraries of London, especially those of the R.H.S., the Royal Agricultural Society of England, and the Royal College of Veterinary Surgeons, that led to the first edition of this book in 1953.

In those days Britain had perhaps the finest organic farming periodical in the world, the quarterly *The Farmer* owned and edited by the late F. W. Newman Turner, whose book *Fertility Farming* I had 'nursed' into print on behalf of Faber and Faber. This book probably started more farmers farming without chemicals when it first came out in 1951 than any other, and it was followed by *Fertility Pastures* and *Herdmanship* which was the first 'nature cure' book for cattle. Newman Turner grew comfrey for his herbal treatments, especially for sterility in Jersey cows caused by being fed too much concentrate to force high milk yields, and he suggested a comfrey yield trial.

Today when *The Daily Telegraph* runs motor boat races round Britain, *The Observer* singlehanded yacht races across the Atlantic, and *The Sunday Times* round the world, we can easily forget that *The Farmer* was the first in the field. The Russian Comfrey Race of 1954 was *The Farmer*'s finest hour. But the journal folded in 1957, lamented like *Picture Post* and *The News Chronicle*.

Unlike the much later *Daily Express* Power Boat Race, with the massive advertising from petrol and sparking plug companies, there was no way in which *The Farmer* could have gained any advertisements. For Newman Turner, a Quaker like Henry Doubleday, refused as a matter of principle to accept advertising for chemical fertilisers or pesticides, but Messrs. Websters' Nurseries took a single column inch in the Spring 1953 number which launched the event.

The first target was the 12 ton an acre yield secured by the Hannah Dairy Research Institute in 1944, with *S. asperrimum* planted in grass. Next came the 1936 record from Holland, where *S. officinale* yielded 36 tons and was blamed for not reaching Henry Doubleday's figure and a 50 ton an acre yield for *S. asperrimum*, not in grass from Lyngby in Denmark in 1947, with Henry Doubleday's 100 tons an acre the final goal, which for all we knew then could be waiting by the end of the season.

Yield figures for wheat, potatoes, or any crop that is harvested and sold are easily gathered, but the only way to measure a fodder crop that is cut daily and fed to stock is to select twenty representative plants and weigh them at every cut through the season. It was hoped to arrange official observers from the nearest Farm Institute, Young Farmers' Club, or N.A.A.S. Agricultural Officer, but this was rarely possible, though Dr. T. Bakker, the Dutch Agricultural Attaché, witnessed one of Newman Turner's cuts.

The spring of 1954 was dry and cold, and it was followed by the coldest summer since 1903, and except for the overseas plots all had a relatively poor season, during which I visited F. Newman Turner, J. Lackenby, E. V. Stephenson, J. C. Quick, Mrs. P. Greer, P. Weir, and I. G. MacDonald, and witnessed a cut each time. The following table shows the results of the first year's Trial:

1954 COMFREY RACE RESULTS

Age of plot	No. of cuts	Name of grower	tons	cwt.	lb.	Date of last cut
Unknown	5	F. Newman Turner, Shaftesbury, Dorset	58	9	2	4 Dec.
4th Year	4	J. Lackenby, Middlesbrough, Yorkshire	53	14	42	10 Nov.
4th Year	5	S. H. Statham, Pinner, Middlesex	43	5	80	14 Nov.
2nd Year	5	E. V. Stephenson, Hull, Yorkshire	33	2	76	15 Nov.
2nd Year	3	J. C. Quick, Exeter, Devon	30	14	90	25 Aug.
2nd Year	6	Mrs. P. B. Greer, Layer-de-la-Haye, Essex	28	14	81	22 Oct.
1st Year	5	Mrs. M. Ridsdale, Rhodesia	24	13	14	29 Nov.
3rd Year	5	Mrs. G. Furness, Burnham, Somerset	24	12	62	13 Nov.
2nd Year	7	P. Weir, Alton, Hampshire	22	17	37	7 Nov.
1st Year	3	H. Dunley-Owen, Rhodesia	21	15	44	30 Aug.
2nd Year	6	I. MacDonald, Goudhurst, Kent	21	10	94	25 Nov.
2nd Year	6	P. Bence-Jones, Eire	18	15	108	30 Nov.
3rd Year	4	J. C. Wylie, Dumfries	16	0	110	8 Oct.
2nd Year	4	Miss K. Arundel, Cardigan	14	4	57	6 Oct.
2nd Year	5	Y. F. C. Holbrook, Ipswich, Suffolk	13	3	96	12 Oct.

These figures can only be a record of what the plants which were grown will yield on that particular soil, on that particular manurial treatment, in that particular season. Any orthodox research station will scorn the hundredweights and pounds, but after long experience of claims for comfrey yields, I insist on them as evidence that something has been cut and weighed. The reports came in cut by cut in pounds and ounces for each plant weighed and my late father, W. D. Hills, B.Sc., worked them out per acre from the various spacings. I am prepared to believe the man who produces a list of plant by plant weights for five or six cuts that add up to 95 tons 7 cwt, and 13 pounds, or 102 tons, 1 cwt. 9 lb., but not the man who produces a round figure of 100 tons an acre in Britain. This applies of course to the low yields on Research Stations in any country, for just as those who grow comfrey well tend to round up their figures and guess high, or quote from the past, the orthodox, who are always prejudiced against this 'flying saucer of agriculture', guess low.

In this first season I saw more different comfrey plots than ever before, and it taught me that I was wrong when I attributed the difference in stem thickness and yield to rich or poor soil and neglected cutting. I had assumed that when Kew regarded comfrey as a species they were right, though I could see it was a variable one, and every one of the individual growers assumed that what they grew was the only cultivated comfrey.

Newman Turner, at Ferne Farm, Shaftesbury, had tall strong plants with thin, pointed leaves, hollow stems and a resemblance to the wild *S. officinale*, especially in their tendency to catch Comfrey Rust (*Melampsorella symphyti*, the only serious disease), while Jim Lackenby, who unfortunately killed his plot completely by folding pigs on it, Mrs. Greer, Paul Weir and Ian MacDonald all had my Southery plants, which I had sold to them. The widest variation was in Vernon Stephenson's plants, grown by J. C. Quick and the bottom four growers on the table. To me it was then obvious that what we had was a hybrid, and that those who buy plants that are split or grown from root cuttings from mixed hybrids are going to have yields that vary according to whether their dozen or even hundred was increased from a productive or non-productive seedling. This was supported by the fact that John Quick's two acres at Exeter was almost all a thin stemmed pointed leaved and very early variation of what I now called 'the Stephenson Strain', and had he taken his last cut his yield would have beaten the mixed parent.

In 1955 we ran the trial again, with the competitors including both old enthusiasts and new entries (see overleaf).

The sensational revelation of this trial was the establishment of the fact that near the equator the day length is equal, with sunset about 6 p.m., and comfrey can be cut all the year round, provided the water supply is kept up. In Rhodesia and Zambia the crop would keep growing, but the cold weather, like a warm English autumn from June to October with drought, fetched the yields down to single tons an acre. Mr. J. McInnes, Secretary of the Kenya Milk Recording Scheme had rainfall enough, and considered that comfrey in Kenya kept two cows in milk where one starved before, providing the high protein part of the ration, fed

with Napier Fodder, a kind of fodder sugar cane, to balance up the
starch equivalent.

1955 COMFREY RACE RESULTS

Age of plot	No. of cuts	Name of grower	tons	cwt.	lb.	Date of last cut
2nd Year	12	J. McInnes, Nakuru, Kenya	124	10	101	1 Oct.
Unknown	4	F. Newman Turner, Shaftesbury, Dorset	67	16	55	5 Oct.
2nd Year	6	J. King, Waimate, New Zealand	62	3	9	24 May
2nd Year	6	L. Fairchild, Chingola, Zambia	55	6	28	21 May
2nd Year	6	Mrs. M. Ridsdale, Rhodesia	52	13	16	23 April
2nd Year	5	M. Dunley-Owen, Rhodesia	49	0	63	5 Feb.
4th Year	6	Sir Philip Christison, Melrose	36	2	13	31 Oct.
3rd Year	5	I. MacDonald, Goudhurst, Kent	32	2	96	31 Oct.
3rd Year	5	P. Bence-Jones, Eire	31	16	97	8 Nov.
17th Year	4	E. V. Stephenson, Yorkshire	25	15	15	10 Oct.
4th Year	4	Mrs. P. B. Greer, Layer-de-la-Haye, Essex	25	13	37	14 Oct.
2nd Year	5	Mrs. M. Owen, Umberleigh, Devon	22	9	106	14 Oct.
2nd Year	5	C. Rogers, St. Austell, Cornwall	20	0	81	12 Oct.
3rd Year	6	P. Weir, Alton, Hampshire	16	10	57	6 Oct.
3rd Year	5	Y. F. C. Holbrook, Ipswich, Suffolk	14	5	103	11 Nov.

1956 COMFREY RACE RESULTS

Age of plot	No. of cuts	Name of grower	tons	cwt.	lb.	Date of last cut
3rd Year	9	T. Henson, North Island, New Zealand	124	2	48	30 Aug.
3rd Year	10	L. Fairchild, Chingola, Zambia	85	2	37	7 Sept.
3rd Year	11	Mrs. M. Ridsdale, Rhodesia	78	0	44	18 Aug.
3rd Year	10	J. McInnes, Nakuru, Kenya	68	12	6	1 July
3rd Year	4	J. Rigg, Wareham, Dorset	60	5	101	12 Oct.
2nd Year	7	C. Moore, Ngong, Kenya	49	7	70	23 Feb.
2nd Year	5	L. Willing, Victoria, British Columbia, Canada	46	1	12	5 Oct.
18th Year	5	E. V. Stephenson, Hull, Yorkshire	42	19	8	3 Nov.
4th Year	6	Sir Philip Christison, Melrose	39	16	110	18 Oct.
3rd Year	4	T. Walmsley, Thorpe-le-Soken, Essex	32	3	4	3 Oct.
2nd Year	5	H. Williams, Biddenden, Kent	39	11	5	21 Oct.
2nd Year	6	A. G. King, East Ham, London E6	27	15	0	4 Oct.
3rd Year	5	Miss Owen, Umberleigh, Devon	22	5	79	28 Oct.
3rd Year	5	Paul Weir, Alton, Hampshire	21	1	44	19 Oct.
3rd Year	3	C. Rogers, St. Austell, Cornwall	15	16	44	11 Oct.

Again in the sub-tropical North Island of New Zealand, the daylength and the moisture scored over the 100 tons an acre for the Southery Strain. Mr. T. Henson of Palmerston North ran deep-litter poultry, manuring his plants heavily every time he cleaned out with a weed-suppressing mulch, rich in nitrogen, and used his crop for pig and poultry green food.

Mr. Fairchild, a bacteriologist at Chingola Hospital, worked out a modification of this deep litter system for tropical climates, that depends on the round the year supply of high protein, low fibre green food from comfrey. Native poultry can manage without green fodder in the dry season, but comfrey made it possible to use European and American breeds for a higher standard of eggs and table birds. In Mr. Fairchild's opinion, had comfrey been used, there need have been no failure for the Gambia egg scheme, which vied with groundnuts in the late 1940s as grumbling blocks for the Labour Government. Mrs. Ridsdale was also feeding comfrey to poultry and making very considerable savings in meal.

After saving Mr. McInnes's Jersey herd the year the Long Rains failed and there was nothing green but the comfrey field, which had got its roots down ten feet to water, his whole crop dried out. The pyrethrum eelworm, *Pratylenchus destructor*, one of the migratory species, found that it could attack comfrey and slaughtered it. This is why Kenya is not a country of comfrey growers, because so much of their land has grown pyrethrum and built up a stock of this versatile nematode. Rhodesia and Zambia are free from the pest and there comfrey grows extensively. The largest field in the world until quite recently was 25 acres at Mteroshanga, Rhodesia, owned by Mr. J. P. Phillips who uses it for feeding bullocks.

This particular plot later secured another world record by producing 100 tons an acre a year for 17 years running, until there was a severe drought that dried the roots completely. Though the termite or white ant will not normally eat living roots, this is because of their moisture content, and when the long droughts of Africa dessicate roots to dry wood, they destroy them as effectively as they will unguarded furniture. They did not however kill the whole field and it is gradually being replanted.

In Britain the first comfrey trial showed that any yield over 50 tons an acre was good, and 60 or more was excellent, while common yields of established plots ranged from 20 to 45 tons an acre. Which, as Mr. J. C. Quick's foreman at Exeter said, is 'one hell of a lot of pig feed'.

3. The comfrey research station

In 1954 when the first edition of *Russian Comfrey* sold out and they began reprinting, the Managing Director of Messrs. Bodie Seeds Ltd. of Canada, a Mr. A. H. A. Lasker, wrote asking me to export 5,000 comfrey plants to him. I had none of my own, but I persuaded Mrs. Peggy Greer to take the order, and stayed at Layer-de-la-Haye to help dig, cut up and wash for inspection by the National Agricultural Advisory Service this huge order, which occupied eight tea chests lavishly labelled and corded.

By the time I had fought the long battle that almost every export order of plants demands, I knew Mr. Lasker rather well, and we had decided to call this Southery Strain, grown by Mrs. Greer, 'Quaker Comfrey' in Canada and the United States, to avoid the Cold War handicap of *Russian* for a crop that 'chose freedom' in 1971. He knew that it was my dream to carry on the research that had ended when my health gave out in 1951 and Southery Nurseries closed down, so he gave me a ton of lucerne seed of a variety barred to Britain by dollar shortage, which made his gift to me tax-free and cost only the freight.

At the time I was living with my father and mother at Barnet with my uncle Gordon Saunders and earning my living as a free-lance gardening writer, and reader of farming and gardening books for Faber and Faber, which made this about the most awkward gift a struggling writer could ever receive. The ton of seed reached London docks, and hit Regulation 365 which then controlled food parcels for Britain, and laid down that these gifts must not weigh more than 22 lb. and be 'for personal use only'. The only way I could have used a ton of lucerne seed personally was to have sown it on 50 acres, but the £275 that a famous farm seedsman was willing to pay for it would be enough to start a Research Station, even though it would be one of the smallest in the world.

Two M.P.s, Mr. C. Allport (now Lord Allport), Member for Colchester, and Mr. Reginald Maudling, Member for Barnet, both fought hard for me. I had a letter in the *New Statesman*, an article in *Time and Tide* and a reporter from *The Morning Post* called to see me, but did not use the story in his paper which then sank without trace into *The Daily Telegraph*. It was all in vain, and despite long-range telephone calls from Mr. Lasker to the Canadian High Commissioner, this generous gift from Canada lay at the docks awaiting a British 'Boston Tea Party'.

Then a second generous gift arrived at the Regulation 365 barrier. While the battle of the lucerne seed had been raging, an American wild animal dealer gave a nice tame black bear to an old friend in London, whose wife objected to its 'personal use' as a pet. Over a hundredweight of bear sitting up and begging for dockers' sandwiches and posing with Teddy Bear appeal for Fleet Street photographers, soon tore away the red tape. So it ambled away on a chain through the dock gates to a new life in the children's corner of a zoo, closely pursued by my ton of lucerne seed.

We moved to Bocking in December 1954 after an attempt to find a house in Coggeshall, and bought No. 20 Convent Lane, a typical suburban semi-detached, built in 1939. With the money from the sale of the seed, I leased the present Trial Ground at £10 a year for ten years, when it was only about three-quarters of an acre, paid for its fencing, and the printing of *Comfrey Report No. 1*. The main path is sited down the middle because this was where the lorries drove down to the gravel pit that is now a lovely angling lake and bird sanctuary, and it was too hard for the stinking, stammering old Trusty Tractor that I hired to break up the matted grass over poor clay and stony sand.

It paid for the labour cost (then 3 shillings an hour—15p in to-day's money) of planting the comfrey strains that the growers of England gave me to try one against the other and to find any potentially record-breaking clones that could have survived from the days of Henry Doubleday. One of my first trips was to Cogge-shall, where I found Henry's land and gathered all that I could find in the hedgerows, strangled by grass but still alive.

I needed a name for the informal organization that was growing out of the fan-mail from my book and my articles on comfrey which invariably cost more in typists' time and postage than the money they earned. So by permission of Thomas Doubleday, I called it 'The Henry Doubleday Research Association' even though it then had no members, no subscription and only a share in my wheelbarrow and garden tools.

By the second summer the plants had grown enough to make it clear that the only answer to the problem of about thirty distinct varieties, with only one species name, *Symphytum peregrinum*, between them was to give them 'cultivar' names, which all hybrids have to have, whether they are of garden or natural origin from chance crosses or are bred by a raiser. Just as the fruit tree stocks from East Malling Research Station are given names like 'Malling No. IX' which is good dwarfing stock for apples, and one of the most famous late brussels sprouts is Cambridge No. 5, I decided to give the comfreys Bocking Numbers, for, like Kodak, 'Bocking' can be said in any language.

The first one I was sure of was a variation in the Newman Turner strain, with very pointed leaves, a tendency to fold inwards from the sides, and dark red flowers, and so I called this 'Bocking No. 1'. After 25 years of looking at plants, including rather more than 1,500 alpines, I had some knowledge of plant identification, so I bought the Royal Horticultural Society's colour chart, which is a number of loose sheets of glossy paper each printed accurately with oblongs of colours, in sequence from dark to pale. It cost £3, which was a large sum then, and in the open with a wind blowing it was about the most awkward thing to handle that can possibly be imagined. I had my eyesight tested to make sure that my colour vision was normal, for I had been rejected as an air-gunner on eyesight in 1940, and attacked the problem.

There were two commercial strains, the Webster and the Stephenson, and a number of 'Survivals' in hedges as well as the main one at Ferne Farm grown by F. Newman Turner, and the numbers in each strain are not consecutive because they were allotted when it was clear that a variation was distinct enough to be separated. Roughly speaking the variations followed either *Symphytum officinale* with thick stems, many of them solid, and leaves which extend down these stems as a kind of fin, described botanically as 'decurrent', (like the stems of the lovely part hardy orange climber from Chile, *Mutisia decurrens*) or *S. asperrimum*. This started into growth 10 to 14 days earlier, and had thin stems with no wings at all. All strains contained both types, and all had two habits—the 'fountain of leaves' stage, like the illustration in Suttons' catalogue, and the tall flowering stage when the crop was allowed to run past its best in terms of protein production, but ideal for identification.

FERNE FARM SURVIVAL

This was supplied by F. Newman Turner, then of Ferne Farm, Shaftesbury, Dorset. It dates from when his farm was a racing stable, and his headlands and odd corners contain a widely varied collection of Symphytums.

The plants supplied are from his plot that yielded 58 tons an acre in 1954 and 67 tons in 1955. Each strain appears to contain a most common clone, which will be referred to as its 'dominant'.

Bocking No. 16

This is the dominant in the above strain. Its flower stems are stout, the wings are broad at the leaf axils and taper sharply, they commonly merge with the stem at a point between half and three-quarters of the distance between the leaves. The leaves on the flower stems are alternate and are waved at the edges. The flower colour is Mauve, 633/1 fading at 633/3 and, especially at the skirt of the bloom, to almost white.

The normal, as distinct from flower stem leaves, are pointed and inclined to fold inwards so that they appear narrower than they are. The proportion of width measured across the broadest part of the leaf to length measured from the end of the stalk to the tip is 5 to 12. This proportionate measurement is used in all subsequent accounts.

Bocking No. 1

The buds show colour first as a dark red, Indian Lake 826/1 and open to Solferino Purple 26/1 fading to 26/3. The effect is of crimson with a little magenta.

The flower stems are relatively weak and come off from the sides of the plant, the wings are small and the stem leaves are alternate but paired behind the flower cluster.

The leaves are sharply pointed and slightly serrated, with a little waving they are inclined to fold towards the centre, reducing apparent width. Their proportion is 6 to 12. It appears to be about 10 per cent of the strain.

Bocking No. 17

In leaf shape and proportion this appears to be near No. 1, but the

Fig. 4 Bocking No. 17 has tiny flowers and the liability to rust that makes the Ferne Farm strain, like most hedgerow survivors, bad bargains even though they can be dug free.

flower stems are wingless, or the wings are mere indications. The
flower colour is Solferino Purple 26/1 but persists as streaks and
patches on the fading bloom. These flowers are smaller than the
type and are bell mouthed instead of puckered inwards like all the
other variations. Their simple tube is unlike any other comfrey
flower either observed or in botanical engravings.

These three variations complete the Ferne Farm Survival as
grown at Bocking; others could be collected at Ferne, but these are
the leaders.

THE STEPHENSON STRAIN

This was started by the late Kenneth Crawley of Lockerbie,
Dumfries, who began growing a Webster strain about 1938; he also
bought in large quantities of Survival plants. He grew $4\frac{1}{2}$ acres of
it at one time, the largest British planting, but this was destroyed
after his death. It was sold by E. V. Stephenson of Hunsley
House Stud, Little Weighton, near Hull.

Bocking No. 14

This is the dominant in the Stephenson strain, 80 to 90 per cent.
The flower stems are slender and frequent and are entirely wingless. The flowers are Imperial Purple 33/3 fading to Lilac Purple
031/3. The leaves are pointed, slightly serrated at the edges and
vary in proportion from 5 to 12 and 3 to 6.

This is also the clone presented by Mr. W. Holmes of the
Hannah Dairy Research Institute to the Holbrook Young Farmers'
Club for their trial from his survivals. Its flower colour is not blue
as stated by Mr. Holmes in *Agriculture* for February 1946.
Because his trials were undertaken in grass for an unmeasured
proportion of the half acre devoted to the crop, and he used close
planting, his results cannot be compared with those of good
farmers.

The balance of the Stephenson Strain is made up of variations
found also in the Webster, the two stemmy and small winged or

wingless variations, Nos. 5 and 7, plus the thick stemmed winged varieties Nos. 4 and 6. There is, however, one special variation.

Fig. 5   Bocking No. 14 takes after *Symphytum asperrimum* in flower stem habit. It is early, rust resistant, and high in potash and allantoin, the healing principle.

Bocking No. 2

The leaves are round tipped and held horizontally from the stout upright flower stem. Their proportion is 4 to 7 and the bristles on the upper surface are so closely set that they give them a grey, mealy appearance entirely unlike the dark green of normal healthy comfrey. The flower stems are wingless and the flowers are Imperial Purple 33/3 when first open, and pale rapidly until they are white with a hint of magenta. Mr. Stephenson regards this variety as a 'rogue'; pigs eat it, but horses on the whole prefer No. 14, which gives a much higher yield.

Fig. 6   Bocking No. 2 is the nearest to Henry Doubleday's plant in flower colour and shape, but it is without the racing speed of the original F_1 hybrid.

THE WEBSTER STRAIN

This is the most popular commercial strain, stated by the late R. O. Webster to have been imported by his father from St. Petersburg in Russia in 1900. The Gibson strain, which has now yielded 124 tons an acre in 12 cuts at Nakuru, Kenya, is a selection of the plant, has 12 months cutting cycle in that climate and is merely from Webster plants imported into Guernsey before 1914.

THE BOCKING MIXTURE

This is the Webster Strain with the low yielders removed from a stock of 500 plants, established by the writer at Southery Nurseries, Southery, near Downham Market, Norfolk, in 1949 on a research project to develop new crops for grass drying organized by the late P. Gordon Saunders, then Chairman of the National Farmers Union Crop Drying Committee.

This improved selection was supplied to many experimenters, including Mr. I. G. MacDonald and Mrs. P. B. Greer. This strain is now the most widely grown in Australia, New Zealand and all parts of Africa. Its characteristics are large leaves and thick stem, with flower colour variations, and some in growth speed. The regularity and higher average yield of Bocking No. 4, however, shows up when the mixture and the pure clone are planted side by side, as at Whipsnade Zoo where about 2½ acres were grown for feeding elephants, hippos, rhinos and giraffes.

Bocking No. 4

This is the dominant in the strain, about 50 to 60 per cent. The flower colour is Bishops Violet 34/3 when fully open. It has strong stems and small wings. The leaves are broad and round tipped, their proportion is 5 to 10, but they have no incurling, therefore they appear far wider than a No. 1 for example. The edges are unserrated, and the veins are prominent, with bristles thickest on the underside so that they appear smooth. At leafy stage these leaves are very large, recovering rapidly after cutting. The stems, as in all the variations under trial, are solid (see Fig. 7 overleaf).

Bocking No. 6

Very near to No. 4 but with flowers Imperial Purple 33/3 when first open fading until the impression is of a pale pink rather than a pale purple. The habit at stage two is rather more upright. It is possible that these two are near enough to be lumped together as the differences may be too small to be significant.

Bocking No. 8

This is a minor variation, distinguished by the narrower leaves on the flower stems. These are sharply pointed and slightly incurved, and their proportion is 1 to 3, up to $3\frac{1}{2}$ to 10. These stems are winged and the flower colour is Bishops Violet 34/3 when the flowers first open. The first stage leaves are large and strong but about 4 to $9\frac{1}{2}$ proportion to the standard 'length twice the width of

Fig. 7   Bocking No. 4 has thick stems like *Symphytum officinale*, but without the distinctive 'wings'. It is preferred by poultry and for human food, with more protein and less allantoin.

the leaf at the widest part' which is the Webster strain standard. It appears to be the most attacked by virus.

Bocking No. 10

Distinct in its flower colour, which is Straw Yellow 604/3 and persists as darker markings when the flowers have faded. It has an upright habit, rather more but slimmer stems than a No. 4, and the wings begin as wide fillets but taper sharply off between the opposite leaves though they continue as thin strip. The stem leaves are 2 to 6 in proportion but the widest part is about a fifth of the way down from the stem and the remainder tapers to a point. The stage one leaves are a normal 1 to 2 proportion.

Bocking No. 11

The stem leaves of this variation are very deeply notched and waved, wings fairly prominent and habit upright but with fewer and thicker stems than a No. 10. The flower colour is Solferino Purple 26/2 when fully open, a shade paler than No. 1 but the reddest colour in the Webster strain, and when the flowers have grown pale with age, the effect is that of almost a rose pink or salmon. The stage one leaves are wide and strong, a proportion of 6 to 11 is common.

Bocking No. 9

The first of the minor variations in the Webster strain, with very much serrated leaves markedly waved at the edges. Otherwise identical with No. 8.

Bocking No. 3

Perhaps the most fantastic variation of all, found rarely in Webster but more common in the selection of broad leaved variations made by I. G. MacDonald called by him 'MacDonald Broad' and the Gibson stock, which also contains more No. 9s. Its flower stems are the thickest of any with wide wings, the flower colour is Lilac Purple 031/3, and the stem leaves are waved at the edges towards the flower head. The lower leaves on these stems are deeply veined, bluntly pointed and very broad 7 to 12 with no incurving. The weight of these stems appear to prevent their being held upright like those of a lighter type and their prostrate habit could cause trouble in mechanical cutting. Now regarded as a rogue.

Bocking No. 5

A wingless Webster variation which proved so near to No. 14 as to be not worth separation. The leaves are pointed ovals with slight serrations, $3\frac{1}{2}$ to $7\frac{1}{2}$ proportion; the stems are slender and produced in great numbers among the main leaves, the habit is upright. The buds show colour as Garnet Lake 828/2 and open to Lilac Purple 031/1 but fade from 031/3 to almost white.

Bocking No. 7

The second wingless Webster, the two make up about 1 per cent of the strain. The stage one leaves of this variation are rather less tapered than the average so though longer and narrower, proportion $3\frac{1}{2}$ to 9, the weight is there. They appear smoother surfaced than normal and are markedly veined and waved, resembling those illustrated in Suttons' Farm Seeds catalogue for 1878. The stems are light, upright and wingless, and the flower colour is Violet 36/3 when fully open, the bluest of all the Websters.

MISCELLANEOUS VARIATIONS

Bocking No. 12

This plant is surviving at Abbey Farm, Coggeshall, from the hedgerow remains of a planting before 1900. The flowers are Bishops Violet 34/3 when fully open and the wings are small. The stage one leaves appear to have a 1 to 2 proportion. Except for slightly thicker stems it is so near Bocking 14 that they are not worth separating.

Bocking No. 13

This has been identified botanically as true *S. asperrimum*. The flowers are Rose Bengal 25/3 on the upper portions, and pure Cobalt 44/2 on the skirt. They are not held in a close cluster, but spaced as shown in Plate 929 of Curtis. The strain, or rather species, for all plants are identical, was sent in to us by a Mrs. Jennens who was greatly dissatisfied with its performance. The flower stems are winged and the leaves very mealy from thick bristle growth.

Messrs. Pritchard, the suppliers, stated that the plants were imported from Messrs. Ruys of Dedemsvaart, Holland, and it appears likely that this is the German 'Binewald', the 'Porkin' of Denmark and the species grown by Askov, which has been giving poor results on research stations in Europe ever since its introduction by James Grant. Messrs. Pritchard sell it only as border plant.

Bocking No. 15

A rogue nicknamed 'Stephenson Sprawler'. This has thick prostrate stems and prominent wings coming out into triangles at the axils. The leaves are serrated, waved and relatively narrow, $2\frac{1}{2}$ to 6 on the stems. The paired leaves behind the flower head have the *S. officinale* angle. The flower colour is Imperial Purple 33/3. It runs to flower and stem very fast.

Bocking No. 18

A rogue from the Gibson stock of Webster strain. It has stiff upright stems which are short jointed and with the leaf wings extending between the leaves. There is reddening of the stem as the flowers develop. The leaves are deeply veined and round tipped with the hairs close together giving a grey effect. The flower colour is Cyclamen Purple 30/1 paling to 30/3 as they are fully open. The lower leaves spread flat on the ground and though they can grow quite large, they miss the mower on a farm scale and are awkward to gather up and cut with shears or a scythe or sickle on a garden one.

Bocking No. 19

The deepest colour in the Webster Strain, Magenta Purple 030/2, otherwise resembling a No. 21. Runs fast to stems.

Bocking No. 20

This was obtained from Messrs. Pritchard of Christchurch as *Symphytum bohemicum*, a brick-red flowered species of modest growth suitable for the herbaceous border.

Bocking No. 21

The 'Sprawler' in the Webster Strain, very near No. 15 but with Bishops Violet 36/3 flowers when fully open. Slightly more upright, pointed leaves and runs to stem quickly.

Symphytum officinale

Descriptions of this species can be found in any botanical work. Its flowers are ¾ inch long and cream-yellow. They can be purple but it can be identified by the wide wings that continue right down the flower stems from leaf to leaf, and the pointed long, narrow leaves.

Our first task was to find how far the yield of mixed plots was being pulled down by the less vigorous variations. Even the best comfrey mixture could be like everyone who leaves a university in a year—there may be students who were sent down as well as those who graduate with honours. When a single plant is split for offsets and root cuttings, this may mean a hundred identical versions of this particular specimen. In some cases a customer could get a dozen or more plants all from one indifferent or poor yielder.

So we spent our first eight years sorting the plants into the different flower colours and habits, getting them established and cutting and weighing them kind by kind for five of these seasons, on our sandy soil, but with the kind of manuring, liming and weeding that will grow a good comfrey plot anywhere. We did not continue cutting the poor yielders right through the full period, so the yields for the missing years are averaged to give a fair comparison. The following tables are arranged in weight order, and relate to *clones* propagated by root cuttings and division.

WEBSTER STRAIN

BOCKING NO. 4		
Year	*tons*	*cwt.*	*lb.*
1957	30	11	75
1958	50	10	53
1959	25	10	44
1960	33	17	51
1961	29	16	104
Total	170	6	103
Average	34	1	43

Bocking No. 4 was very near Bocking No. 6, which had pinker flowers, Bocking No. 10, which was identical but yellow flowered, and No. 11 which was quite a good salmon shade. So we decided to stick to the commonest and strongest kind as a pure clone, leaving the rest in the standard mixture. This averaged the following yield over the same five years, including 1959 which was equally dry for all variations.

BOCKING MIXTURE		
Year	*tons*	*cwt.*	*lb.*
1957	24	2	4
1958	39	8	66
1959	19	8	100
1960	35	3	88
1961	32	8	28
Total	150	11	62
Average	30	2	35

On better land, both Bocking No. 4 and Bocking Mixture can achieve higher yields. General Sir Philip Christison, who became Vice-President of the Henry Doubleday Research Association when it was reformed into a Registered Charity in 1958,* grew it for pig feeding on his farm at Melrose, Scotland, for many years, and secured the following yield, over four years:

BOCKING MIXTURE AT MELROSE

Year	tons	cwt.	lb.
1957	56	12	87
1958	42	8	23
1959	39	19	35
1960	34	2	69
Total	173	2	102
Average	43	5	81

A still higher yield was secured by Leonard Willing of Victoria B.C., a Canadian Member of the H.D.R.A. with 'Quaker Comfrey' mixture from the original export. This has the distinction of being officially cut and weighed for three years by The Dominion Experimental Farm, Saskatoon, Saskatchewan. The field was planted in June 1955 at three feet apart each way, or 4,840 plants an acre.

REPORT BY DOMINION EXPERIMENTAL FARMS, SASKATOON, SASKATCHEWAN, CANADA

Soil

The soil is a light sandy loam subject to summer drought. The area received a liberal dressing of chicken manure, mulched on the surface after the plants were set out. A light sprinkling of wood

* The Association now has over 5,000 members in all countries, including two groups in Australia and one in India. Its subscription is £3 a year which brings the latest news of comfrey research in a Quarterly Newsletter, and many reports, as well as advice for members, in all fields of operation. The work has expanded to include all aspects of farming and gardening without chemicals, especially biological and other ecologically sound methods of pest control, pollution, diet and wholefood. The development of the agricultural, horticultural and medicinal aspects of comfrey are still major objectives.

ashes and ground limestone was applied to the plot in the spring of 1956. No other fertilizers were applied.

Irrigation

The general area is characterized by very dry summers, and in 1958 practically no rain occurred during the growing season. Water from a small irrigation system was applied during the summer months. Although no actual records were kept, Mr. Willing estimated that about $1\frac{1}{2}$ inches of water were applied every 3 to 4 weeks, with a total of about 8 to 10 inches applied during June, July and August each year.

Cultivation

A light cultivation was given during the early growth of the plants to keep down weeds. No cultivation has been required after the first year of establishment and the comfrey has successfully competed against all weeds except a patch of couch grass.

Sampling

The Field Crops Branch became interested in the comfrey planted by Mr. Willing in 1955. It was felt some preliminary information should be obtained by observing growth and recording yield data. No attempt was made to carry out replicated field trials but in 1956 a test plot was selected at random containing two rows of ten plants each. Guard rows were left on each side and one end. Plants Nos. 1 and 11 were at the end of each row next to the sod headland. The plants were numbered, harvested individually and yields recorded. The attached table gives the green weight yield data taken over three years.

Time of Cutting

The plants were cut when they had made good leafy growth, but just before buds started to appear. Because of the variability noted within the plant population all plants were not at the same physiological growth stage when cut. Some plants headed sooner than others. There appeared to be a wide variation in plant type.

3

Analyses

Samples of the comfrey were analysed for moisture and protein.
The following table gives results:

	Moisture per cent	Crude Protein (Dry) per cent	Crude Protein (Wet Sample) per cent
1955	82·6	22·0	3·8
1956	90·5	26·0	2·6
1958	89·0	28·2	3·1

Feeding Results

Mr. Willing cut and hauled fresh comfrey from the field each day
to his milking cows. He estimated that each cow received approximately 30 pounds per day. The comfrey was fed just before
milking and there was no taint to the milk and no bloat occurred.
When first presented with the fresh forage, the cows did not
appear to relish it. However, by slightly wilting the forage, the
cows would eat it, and after a short time they ate the fresh forage
with relish.

Mr. Willing attempted curing the leaves for hay in a small way.
The forage was cut and spread out on the ground and allowed to
dry. The dried leaves were gathered and stored with mixed grass
hay in the barn. The cows ate the dry comfrey leaves readily along
with the other cured forage.

Frost Resistance

The plants start growth very early in the spring and during the
mild winter of 1958 a clip was actually made in the third week of
March. The plants have survived up to 15 degrees of frost for short
periods (night frost). However, prolonged temperatures below
freezing froze the green leaves black. Temperatures have only gone
down to about 0°F. in the area and there has been no winter
injury of any kind to the plants.

Pests

No diseases or insects have been noted on the plants.

Harvesting and Storing

As indicated, Mr. Willing only hand-cuts sufficient forage each day for a few cows, and most of the literature also indicates that the crop, although used for livestock feed, is grown on a small scale and handled by hand as a soiling crop. It is claimed that it can be cured as silage or hay, but with the high moisture content and low fibre, difficulty would be experienced in curing the crop. Similarly with the 3 × 3 ft. row spacing and the general habit of growth, comfrey would not appear to lend itself too well to mechanical handling with the present forage harvesting equipment.

NORMAN F. PUTNAM
Field Crops Branch

COMFREY YIELDS—DOMINION EXPERIMENTAL FARM
SASKATOON
POUNDS PER PLOT 1956

Plant No.	14 May lb. oz.		18 June lb. oz.		25 July lb. oz.		27 August lb. oz.		5 October lb. oz.		Total lb. oz.	
Row 1												
1	2	12	4	14	6	7	5	15	1	14	21	14
2	1	12	4	4	4	8	5	13	1	15	18	4
3	6	3	4	12	7	1	6	1	2	3	26	4
4	9	8	7	1	6	12	8	9	4	1	35	15
5	0	15	3	7	6	2	7	3	2	11	20	6
6	2	7	5	13	5	12	6	1	3	8	23	9
7	1	1	4	1	5	4	5	13	2	2	18	5
8	6	2	6	3	4	6	7	2	2	9	26	6
9	1	5	2	14	3	6	4	15	1	13	14	5
10	1	11	4	7	4	0	5	10	2	4	18	0
Row 2												
11	3	9	4	10	4	4	5	7	1	5	19	3
12	3	12	5	15	6	5	5	5	2	0	23	5
13	5	6	7	2	5	6	6	8	3	1	27	7
14	1	6	4	0	5	1	6	14	2	11	20	0
15	2	14	5	4	6	8	5	12	2	8	22	14
16	5	12	8	9	5	0	5	10	2	14	27	13
17	0	10	2	10	3	14	5	12	2	3	15	1
18	1	6	3	15	4	0	4	1	1	7	14	13
19	3	9	5	15	4	13	5	5	2	3	21	13
20	0	10	3	7	3	14	4	11	1	10	14	4
Total	62	10	99	3	101	11	118	7	4	14	428	13

POUNDS PER PLOT 1958

Plant No.	6 May lb. oz.		9 June lb. oz.		28 July lb. oz		25 Sept. lb. oz.		Total lb. oz.	
Row 1										
1	3	6	5	4	5	14	10	6	24	14
2	4	14	3	8	4	14	6	8	19	12
3	4	9	4	4	5	4	9	0	23	1
4	6	1	7	4	7	3	15	0	35	8
5	5	13	5	10	6	4	8	4	25	15
6	5	15	6	6	6	7	10	0	28	12
7	4	15	5	0	6	7	7	4	23	10
8	5	0	4	15	7	9	7	5	24	13
9	4	8	3	12	5	0	8	0	21	4
10	3	4	4	5	3	13	5	9	16	15
Row 2										
11	3	12	4	8	4	0	6	14	19	2
12	5	0	6	2	8	7	8	10	28	3
13	6	0	4	15	7	0	9	12	27	11
14	4	5	6	1	8	4	11	2	29	12
15	4	8	5	14	8	0	11	4	29	10
16	4	7	6	1	9	13	10	10	30	15
17	1	9	4	2	5	4	7	1	18	0
18	4	15	4	1	6	1	6	4	21	5
19	5	7	5	13	7	11	8	11	27	10
20	4	14	6	0	6	9	7	4	24	11
Total	93	2	103	13	129	12	174	12	501	7

THREE YEAR SUMMARY
Calculated Tons Per Acre (2,000 lbs. = 1 American ton)

Plant No.	1956	1957	1958	Average tons/acre
Row 1				
1	52·94	31·16	60·20	48·10
2	44·16	48·70	47·80	46·88
3	63·52	31·90	55·81	50·41
4	86·97	94·98	85·91	89·28
5	49·31	59·74	62·77	57·27
6	57·02	66·10	69·58	64·23
7	41·90	45·68	57·17	48·25
8	63·83	52·18	60·05	58·68
9	34·64	44·01	51·42	43·35
10	43·56	32·52	40·99	39·02
Row 2				
11	46·43	34·94	46·28	45·88
12	56·42	44·01	68·21	56·21
13	66·40	70·78	67·00	68·06
14	48·40	58·99	72·00	59·79
15	55·36	57·93	71·69	61·66
16	67·31	68·21	74·87	70·13
17	36·45	39·78	43·56	39·93
18	35·85	45·68	51·58	44·34
19	52·79	57·02	66·85	58·88
20	34·48	44·32	59·74	46·18
Total	1,037·74	1,028·63	1,213·48	
Average	51·89	51·43	60·67	54·66

What is important about the table is the fact that plant 4 in Row 1 averaged 89·28 American tons (2,000 lb.) an acre over the four years, plant 16 in Row 2 averaged 70·13 American tons, while plants 10 and 17 were only scoring just over 39 tons. Because comfrey is a root cutting subject it would be possible to pick the high yielders out of mixed strains where regular cutting and weighing is practised.

COMFREY YIELDS
University of California, Davis

Harvest date	Yield pounds per acre		Percentage protein, dry weight basis
	Fresh	Dry	
(A) 1958			
3 June	104,544	7,318	21·2
1 July	40,656	4,066	24·2
6 August	46,464	5,576	22·3
11 November	39,688	7,144	15·7
Total	231,352	24,104	20·9 (av.)
American Tons	115·676	12·052	
British Tons	103-5 cwt.-72 lb.	10-15 cwt.-24 lb.	
(B) 1967—Old Plot			
26 April	19,482	2,143	26·8
5 May	24,418	2,686	26·2
24 May	26,637	3,303	23·3
6 June	25,410	2,541	25·8
23 June	16,578	2,868	22·1
30 June	13,813	1,851	28·6
24 July	8,716	889	25·6
5 September	8,675	1,735	25·0
16 November	3,969	889	25·0
Total	147,698	18,905	25·4 (av.)
American Tons	73·849	9·452	
British Tons	65-18 cwt.-82 lb.	8-8 cwt.-89 lb.	
(C) 1967—New Plot			
24 May	2,453	363	22·6
23 June	9,620	1,443	25·8
24 July	21,255	2,168	25·6
5 September	11,125	2,225	25·0
6 November	5,893	1,320	25·0
Total	50,346	7,519	24·8 (av.)
American Tons	25·173	3·7595	
British Tons	22-9 cwt.-58 lb.	3-7 cwt.-15 lb.	

It is possible to identify clones by flower colour and habit, and with adequate yield recording, like milk recording dairy cows, it would be possible to multiply a single plant to thousands in the course of a very few years. These thousands would need re-recording to make certain that the particular plant was not a product of a specially favoured position or soil conditions. The Bocking numbered varieties may be only a rough guide to the qualities of cultivated comfrey. It may be found that there are better plants still in the Bocking Mixture or Quaker Comfrey than I have selected from it. Leonard Willing's No. 4 may well be the best yet.

The only modern record of a yield above 100 tons an acre from an official research station comes from Milton D. Miller and Edward Johnson of the Agronomy Extension, University of California, Davis, California, where several large plots of 'Quaker Comfrey' were established for pig feeding experiments (see p. 69).

The world's record yields were both secured with solid stemmed mixtures and they are given below as month by month cuts from 20 average plants, as on the H.D.R.A. trial ground. The day length is not equal on the North Island of New Zealand; the cutting season is about the same length as ours; but they have a warmer summer, and this plot was well fed and cut hard to supply green food from a small area for a large deep litter poultry farm.

T. HENSON, NEW ZEALAND

	tons	cwt.	lb.
October 1957	24	18	109
December	39	19	50
January 1958	17	16	63
March	22	13	87
April	12	8	74
May	6	9	72
Total	124	7	7

J. MCINNES, KENYA

	tons	cwt.	lb.
November 1954	5	18	104
December	6	9	72
January 1955	8	13	0
February	6	8	72
March	7	11	28
April	12	6	37
May	14	18	23
June	14	11	61
July	13	14	22
August	12	12	92
September	10	16	10
October	10	16	10
Total	124	16	83

The second highest yielder over five years at Bocking is Bocking No. 14, which is much earlier starting into growth than No. 4. Its value to Vernon Stephenson was to give early comfrey for the first foals, and at times he covered plants with cloches to bring them on just a little earlier. This particular clone is now the most common in South Africa, because of the many thousands split from a single plant and given away by my wife before our marriage when she lived in Capetown.

STEPHENSON STRAIN
Bocking No. 14

5 years	tons	cwt.	lb.
1957	28	4	49
1958	38	8	66
1959	22	11	5
1960	39	0	53
1961	40	8	17
Total	168	12	78
Average	33	14	15

This particular variety is the most often found in the hedges round fields where comfrey once grew, because, as the analysis figures in the next chapter show, it is the highest in potash and this appears to make it distasteful to rabbits and unattractive to poultry *when it is growing*. It also has the highest resistance to Comfrey Rust (*Melampsorella symphyti*), the only serious disease of the crop, which infects the wild *S. officinale* so badly that this species cannot be grown commercially, except on a small scale in herb gardens. The specimen in the Herb Garden at Kew is (or was up to 1972) a thriving plant of Bocking No. 14 which is also highest in allantoin.

This variety is perhaps the best for garden cultivation, for race and riding horses, for pigs, and for feeding to poultry if wilted well and chaffed. Its high potash makes it of special value as 'instant compost', compost material and liquid manure on a garden scale.

Research to find a cure for Comfrey Rust still continues, and among the remedies tried have been Equisitum preparations, decoctions of infected leaves, heavy composting, hot water treatment as for Mint Rust, flame gunning, and almost all the fungicides. The best so far is Benlate, which has the grave disadvantage of killing out earthworms, but it is a systemic fungicide that gets right inside the plant and knocks out the fungus. For safety it is best to cut the plants to waste rather than feed them to stock during the year of treatment.

The rust is visible at the uredospore stage, when the undersides of the leaves are covered with orange powder, starting usually in June, and spreading until in late July it loosens and blows on the wind. On a garden scale it is best to dig up the attacked plant and dump it in your dustbin, but cutting the foliage as soon as the spores are detected and watering with a strong solution of Jeyes Fluid, or a phenol-based farm disinfectant can cure a starting infection. The rust risk (which is not high where there is no wild comfrey in the area) is greatly reduced by planting Bocking No. 14.

NEWMAN TURNER STRAIN

Bocking No. 16

5 years	tons	cwt.	lb.
1957	25	13	60
1958	42	0	2
1959	23	4	48
1960	28	17	75
1961	29	15	70
Total	149	11	31
Average	29	18	29

Bocking No. 17

5 years	tons	cwt.	lb.
1957	25	18	25
1958	40	18	42
1959	24	3	54
1960	22	10	64
1961	24	6	20
Total	137	16	93
Average	27	11	41

Bocking No. 1

5 years	tons	cwt.	lb.
1957	21	4	5
1958	32	9	10
1959	20	13	27
1960	24	8	51
1961	24	8	51
Total	123	3	32
Average	24	12	79

FERNE FARM RECORD 1954

	tons	cwt.	lb.
12 May	23	19	76
18 June	8	1	34
10 August	10	10	76
19 October	8	16	41
4 December	7	0	50
Total	58	8	53

FERNE FARM RECORD 1955

	tons	cwt.	lb.
15 April	5	7	106
2 June	23	17	41
18 August	24	18	103
5 October	13	10	41
Total	67	14	67

The Ferne Farm plot was behind the cow sheds, very convenient for manuring and cutting, also sheltered. The December cut in 1954 was possible because of a mild autumn, and was taken because it was needed for stock instead of left to die down to build up the crown for the following season. The first cut of 1955 would have been larger if the late growth had been left uncut as usual.

Mr. F. Newman Turner used his bed to provide a kind of 'nature cure' treatment for pedigree cattle, including one Supreme Dairy Show Champion. Jersey cows fed on concentrates to force their gallonage higher and higher can suffer from sterility, and a diet of comfrey and water only could solve this problem, perhaps with the combination of allantoin and Vitamin E that comfrey contains. Those who wish to follow Mr. Newman Turner's system of herbal veterinary treatments and organic farming stock rearing methods will find them in *Herdsmanship* (Faber and Faber, 1954).

His strain was a very level one, with Bocking No. 1 the lowest yielder, but it is so near *S. officinale* that it is the most subject of all to Comfrey Rust. Even for veterinary uses, Bocking No. 14 is a better crop with rust resistance, a rather longer season, and considerably more allantoin.

LOW YIELDING VARIATIONS AND SPECIES

Symphytum asperrimum

Year	tons	cwt.	lb.
1958	20	3	15
1959	21	14	96
1960	20	1	22
1961	29	3	42
Total	91	2	63
Average	22	15	72

Bocking No. 2

Year	tons	cwt.	lb.
1957	14	4	32
1958	25	14	88
1959	16	4	12
Total	56	3	20
Average	18	14	44

Bocking No. *15*			
Year	tons	cwt.	lb.
1957	20	5	16
1959	28	0	97
Total	48	6	1
Average	24	3	1

Bocking No. *20*			
Year	tons	cwt.	lb.
1957	17	2	98
1958	10	0	9
1959	10	10	65
1960	16	5	11
Total	53	19	59
Average	13	9	99

Bocking No. *7*			
Year	tons	cwt.	lb.
1957	17	19	36
1958	14	9	65
1960	20	0	39
Total	52	9	28
Average	17	9	84

Bocking No. *18*			
Year	tons	cwt.	lb.
1959	18	7	28
1961	18	18	15
Total	37	5	43
Average	18	12	78

It is probably possible for a record yield of comfrey to be secured from a single Bocking No. 4, No. 14 or No. 16, just as there are record yields of potatoes from a single seed tuber in contests organized by gardening periodicals that are won every year by the same people. What counts on the farm is the ability of clones to stand up to cutting year after year and average a worth-while yield in good seasons and bad. From the trial at Bocking with all the plants on the same soil, with the same weather, manuring and cultivations, it is possible to make a kind of league table of productivity.

As a rough guide to those who are 'rogueing' comfrey mixtures it should be said that any comfrey which cannot average 25 tons an acre is not worth growing and anyone who gets less yield than that should either improve his cultivation methods, or get rid of the crop.

It is unlikely that any variation on the themes of these varieties will turn out to be remarkably higher in yield, and this is all that is likely to happen from cross- or self-pollinating hybrids. Real differences in yield can only come from the hybrid vigour of a

AVERAGE YIELDS

	tons	cwt.	lb.
Bocking No. 4	34	1	43
Bocking No. 14	33	14	15
Bocking Mixed	30	2	35
Bocking No. 16	29	18	29
Bocking No. 17	27	11	41
Bocking No. 1	24	12	79
Bocking No. 15	24	3	1
Symphytum asperrimum	22	15	72
Bocking No. 2	18	14	44
Bocking No. 18	18	12	78
Bocking No. 7	17	9	84
Bocking No. 20	13	9	99

bi-generic cross, such as the one between *S. asperrimum* and *S. officinale*.

We have tried this on several occasions, and so have our members, but it needs real skill with a camel hair brush and in breaking the flowers apart. We have a small stock of *S. asperrimum* which we would be glad to supply to serious experimenters with experience of plant genetics. Treatment with colchicine to double the chromosomes from 36 to 72 appears likely to produce variations of *S. tuberosum*, which has 72 chromosomes because it is a mutation of *S. officinale*, but not a useful one, for doubling the chromosome number does not always mean doubling the yield. Irradiating comfrey seed with radioactive cobalt would produce still wilder mutations, and these could contain a record-breaking plant which could be increased indefinitely from root cuttings. This would involve growing hundreds of seedlings on for at least three years to bring them into full production so that their yield could be measured. A 'miracle comfrey' would also need analysis to see how the change had affected its mineral and vitamin content.

Some years ago a cross between *S. caucasium* and *S. asperrimum* was obtained from the U.S.S.R. and grown on the H.D.R.A. trial ground, but it proved no more productive than ordinary *S. asperrimum*, for not all first crosses produce hybrid vigour. Seed saved from hybrids, whenever it is set, produces variations on the parents, including all the low producers described earlier.

No comfrey plant, clone or seedling should ever be sold as something special at a higher price until it has been grown for at least four years, not only to establish its productivity, but to be certain that it will maintain its yield year after year on a farm scale when kept clean, cut and fed.

4. The analysis of comfrey

The basic problem of analysis is its cost, and though the H.D.R.A. would have liked to have gone through all the variations of comfrey for minerals, allantoin, vitamins, carbohydrate, fibre and protein, they have no more been able to afford this than the National Vegetable Research Station has for the common vegetables. A figure can be looked up in standard reference books, but no one has undertaken the analysis of all the potato varieties either.

In addition to this problem, we are now so far from Dr. Auguste Voelcker and his 'mucilage', that we know that proteins are made of amino-acids of which ten are essential in our diets, and at the moment of writing in 1973, it cost £36 to measure all of them. The standard tables in *The Composition of Foods* by R. A. McCance and E. M. Widdowson (H.M.S.O., 1960) relate to one variety only of everything. We do not know if potatoes, carrots, onions and what have you, vary from kind to kind; if we did it would be possible to breed for a better balance of amino-acids, as well as yield, appearance, toughness to endure long trips to the customer, and (very rarely) flavour. At present we prefer to guess, though the U.S.A. spent more on finding out what the other side of the Moon was like, than the total they have so far spent on agricultural research.

All that could be afforded by the H.D.R.A. was a set of minerals analyses from the leading varieties. The following figures are from the H.D.R.A. trial ground.

These figures have the disadvantage that they were not from comfrey dried on the same day. The cut-by-cut analysis is from the National Institute of Agricultural Botany, at Cambridge, to whom the H.D.R.A. presented a set of clones. Unfortunately they did not make an October cut, and there is evidence that the mineral content falls in the late autumn, for as comfrey dies down it

THE MINERAL ANALYSIS OF COMFREY

Bocking No. 4		*Bocking No. 15*	
Cut 5 May		*Cut 15 October*	
	per cent		*per cent*
Calcium	2·35	Calcium	2·38
Phosphoric acid	1·25	Phosphoric acid	0·78
Potash	5·04	Potash	6·95
Iron	0·253	Iron	0·23
Manganese p.p.m.	137	Manganese p.p.m.	133
Cobalt	trace	Cobalt, less than 1 p.p.m.	

Bocking No. 14		*Bocking mixture*	
Cut 13 October		Calcium	2·58
Calcium	2·77	Phosphoric acid	1·07
Phosphoric acid	0·75	Potash	5·01
Potash	7·09	Iron	0·457
Iron	0·144	Manganese p.p.m.	201
Cobalt less than 1 p.p.m.		Cobalt	trace

Symphytum officinale

Calcium	1·31
Phosphoric acid	0·72
Potash	3·09
Iron	0·098
Manganese p.p.m.	85

Mixed Bocking clones

	Potash	*Phosphorous*	*Calcium*
	per cent	*per cent*	*per cent*
7 April	7·95	1·25	1·86
15 May	5·94	0·72	2·70
26 June	7·44	1·15	1·81
7 July	8·25	1·01	2·65
6 September	7·83	1·05	3·10

returns its minerals to store in the roots, just as bracken does. This analysis tells us that Bocking No. 14 is probably the richest in potassium, and that the Bocking clones are higher in calcium, manganese and iron than the wild *Symphytum officinale*.

The Nutritional Analysis of Comfrey

The tables in this section are reproduced and calculated from *Rations for Livestock*, Bulletin No. 48, Ministry of Agriculture and Fisheries, obtainable from H.M.S.O. The 'V factor' column in the table of comparative values on p. 81 will be unfamiliar to those with experience of human nutrition, but it relates to the 'percentage availability' of a feeding stuff. The correction is necessary because the full values of the digestible nutriments do not become available for production because of the energy that is wasted in the work of mastication and digestion. The higher the 'V factor' the more the wastage. The figures for 'Russian Comfrey' are for a Webster mixture, while plain 'Comfrey' is *S. asperrimum*, according to Professor H. E. Woodman, author of Bulletin No. 48.

From this we see that a Webster Comfrey and *Symphytum asperrimum* contain less dry matter, ton for ton, than any other fodder crop except Drumhead Cabbage, which has winter availability as a hidden asset. On crude protein, *S. peregrinum*, ton for ton, is beaten by good pasture grass and lucerne, and is level with red clover and Italian rye grass; on carbohydrates it is at the bottom of the list, but it contains less crude fibre than any other crop. Lucerne contains roughly five times as much. Here one can follow the crop across the page in comparison with its fellows, bearing in mind that rape is a quick catch crop, and as such has very many more advantages than slightly more digestible carbohydrates and slightly less digestible crude protein, and that red clover, with not quite double the starch equivalent, is also a nitrogen fixer.

This type of comparison is extremely valuable with purchased feeds, but to give a complete picture one needs a record in terms of how much in nutrimental harvest an acre yields. Labour costs, ease of cultivation and many other factors come in also, so does the extreme variation of soil from farm to farm and season from year to year. The table giving comparative yields is calculated in pounds weight per acre; the ton, the hundredweight and the quarter have

COMPARATIVE ANALYSIS OF COMFREYS AND OTHER FODDER CROPS

Data extracted from
*Bulletin No. 48
Rations for Livestock*
by permission of
H.M. Stationery Office

page	Crop	Average Composition per cent as shown by Chemical Analysis						Digestible Nutrients per cent					Calculated from Digestible Nutrients		
		Dry Matter (1)	Crude Protein (2)	Oil (ether extract) (3)	Carbohydrate (Nitrogen-free extractives) (4)	Crude Fibre (5)	Ash (6)	Digestible Crude Protein (7)	Digestible True Protein (8)	Dig. Oil (Dig. Ether extract) (9)	Digestible Carbohydrate (Dig. Nitrogen-free extractives) (10)	Digestible Fibre (11)	Nutritive Ratio (approx.) (12)	V Factor (13)	Starch Equivalent per 100 lb. (14)
128	Comfrey (Russian)	12·4	3·4	·3	4·9	1·5	2·3	2·04	1·22	·2	3·62	·7	1:2·8	91	5·32
117	Comfrey	11·5	2·5	·3	5·0	1·7	1·5	1·5	·9	·2	3·7	·8	1:3	91	5·2
114	Cabbage (drumhead)	11	1·5	·4	5·9	2·0	1·2	1·1	·9	·2	4·6	1·4	1:6	94	6·6
115	Maize (Green)	19·4	1·7	·5	10·4	5·6	1·0	1·0	·6	·3	6·7	3·1	1:10	83	9·1
115	Rape	14·1	2·8	·8	5·7	3·5	1·3	2·0	1·3	·5	3·9	1·9	1:3	87	6·9
115	Marrowstem Kale (unthinned)	14	2·2	·5	6·9	2·5	1·9	1·7	1·2	·3	6·1	1·6	1:4·9	93	9·1
117	Lucerne (early flower)	24	4·1	·4	9·9	7·2	2·4	3·1	2·0	·1	6·6	3·2	1:3·2	80	10·3
115	Pasture Grass (non-rotational)	20	5·3	1·1	8·9	2·6	2·1	4·5	3·8	·7	7·8	2·1	1:2·5	95	14·7
116	Red Clover	19	3·4	·7	8·1	5·2	1·6	2·5	1·7	·5	6·3	3	1:4	86	10·2
116	Rye Grass (Italian)	25	3·4	1·0	11·6	6·2	2·8	2·1	1·3	·5	7·7	3·6	1:6	85	11·4

not been used because of space difficulties and the complication of the American ton of 2,000 lb. The yields for crops other than the comfreys were extremely difficult to secure; many fodder plants have been left out purely because, like sainfoin, there is no recorded evidence that they produce anything at all. These are kindly selected by the Grassland Research Station (with the exception of Green Maize from *Agriculture* by Sir James A. Scott Watson and James A. More (Oliver and Boyd, ninth edition, 1949), and they are of a moderate yield and a really good one. The writer has never seen a 50 ton per acre crop of marrowstem kale as an example, and the 'as grazed' figure for pasture is for a really good ley of pedigree grasses.

At 20 tons an acre per season, though both comfreys produce more dry matter in tons per acre than a low yield of anything else, except pasture grass, and they lead on crude protein, they are beaten on carbohydrates by everything except low-yielding lucerne, low-yielding rape and also the lower yield of red clover and Italian rye grasses. (These two are lumped together, as pure red clover is rarely grown except for seed.) The same balance holds all across through the digestible nutriments. A new column has been added for the benefit of pig- and poultry-men. Starch equivalent includes digestible fibre—it is of extreme value in calculating the rations of grazing animals, but pigs and poultry digest so little that the total without fibre is included as a nearer approach to what they do digest.

At 50 tons an acre only the record crop of marrowstem kale is ahead on dry matter, and Russian comfrey is over 850 lb. more than the best pasture grass on crude protein. Good lucerne still leads on fibre, and green maize and kale on carbohydrates. At this figure the crop pays the pig- and poultry-man as giving the green fodder vitamins and vegetable protein with the least fibre. It also pays the race horse breeder and riding stable proprietor, with the concealed subsidies of improved condition, and a supply of minerals equal to that of the old long matured hay that stud farmers pay absurd prices for.

Take the yield up to 100 tons an acre, as at the University of California, or in New Zealand and in Kenya where the picture alters, with the crop in cut all the year round, and continual feeding is possible at great saving of labour. Even in Britain or other temperate climates, yields above the 50 tons an acre make it worth organizing the farming programme to fit the crop. Comfrey is like a jet engine, inefficient at low speeds but a winner in the stratosphere. At under 20 tons an acre it is a weed, justifying all that has been said against it. At three times the yield it is a crop deserving the most serious consideration.

The lower the yield of comfrey, the larger loom its many disadvantages. Though it will last over twenty years from a planting, it must be established expensively from offsets or root cuttings instead of cheaply from seed. It is not a winter feed like kales for dairy cattle, it is not a nitrogen fixer like lucerne, and it will not thrive on the thin soils over chalk where this deep rooting legume does best, and its conservation as hay or silage still needs more research.

The economics of agriculture are changing all the time, and when the first edition of this book appeared in 1954, farmers were aiming at self-sufficiency to save imports. In the 1970s our need is to save protein, with the anchovy harvest off the coast of Chile vanished with a change in the Humboldt current and a ban on soya bean exports from the U.S. sending prices soaring. We in the well-fed West use about eight times as much land to grow our food as we need, because we insist on eating animal products.

Spring Tic beans rose from £35 a ton in 1972 to £120 in 1973, and these, like our other stock feed beans, are a source of the concentrated vegetable protein we need for a vegetarian diet tastier than soya beans, which take long cooking and have little flavour. If we are going to 'knit steaks' from vegetable protein, something that will grow in Britain with a 2 ton an acre yield of protein, even if its amino-acid balance is not perfect, could be better value than perfection, with a yield of only 6 cwt. an acre for the new hardy soya bean Fiskeby V.

Comfrey is the fastest vegetable protein builder we have found so far, and it is in theory the best cheap source as food for stock to replace concentrates. The developing countries may well develop as far as feeding their fishmeal to their own under-nourished

Comparative yield per acre calculated from table on page 81. The '

Crop Yield Figures, other than Comfrey, from The Grassland Research Station	Annual yield per acre in tons	Dry Matter Tons (1)	Crude Protein lb. (2)	Oil (Ether Extract) lb. (3)	Carbohydrate (Nitrogen-free Extractives) lb. (4)	Crude Fibre lb. (5)	Ash lb. (6)
Comfrey (Russian)	100	12·4	7,616	672	11,000	3,360	5,152
,,	75	9·3	5,707	404	8,250	2,520	3,864
,,	50	6·2	3,808	336	5,500	1,680	2,576
,,	20	2·49	1,553	134	2,200	672	1,031
Comfrey	100	11·5	5,600	672	11,200	3,808	4,480
,,	75	8·62	4,200	404	8,400	2,856	3,360
,,	50	5·75	2,800	336	5,600	1,904	2,240
,,	20	2·3	1,120	134	2,240	762	896
Cabbage (Drumhead)	high 50	5·5	1,680	448	6,608	2,240	1,344
,,	low 20	2·2	672	179	2,644	896	535
Maize (Green)	high 25	4·84	950	280	5,824	3,136	560
,,	low 10	1·94	382	110	2,330	1,254	224
Rape	high 20	2·82	1,254	357	2,554	1,568	572
,,	low 10	1·41	627	179	1,277	784	236
Marrow-stem Kale (unthinned)	high 50	7·0	2,464	560	7,728	2,800	2,188
	low 15	2·1	740	168	2,318	840	638
Lucerne (early flower)	high 18	3·32	1,658	161	4,000	2,902	965
,,	low 9	1·66	829	80	2,000	1,451	482
Pasture Grass non-rotational	high 25	5·0	2,950	618	4,984	1,450	1,175
	low 12	2·4	1,422	295	2,390	695	566
Red Clover and Italian Rye Grass	high 15	3·3	1,142	286	3,319	1,916	739
	low 8	1·76	610	153	1,768	1,020	394

s are record figures or near, the low ones average farm crops.

Digestible Crude Protein	Digestible True Protein	Dig.: Oil (Dig.: Either extract)	Dig. Carbohydrate (Dig. Nitrogen-free extractives)	Dig. Fibre	Total Starch Equivalent per acre	Total Digestible material per acre columns $(7)+(10)+(11)+(9)\times2\cdot25$	Digestible by Pigs and Poultry Columns $(8)+(10)+(9)\times2\cdot25$
lb.	lb.	lb.	lb.	lb.	lb.	lb.	lb.
(7)	(8)	(9)	(10)	(11)	(14)	(15)	—
4,569	2,736	448	8,108	1,568	11,917	15,253	11,852
3,426	2,052	336	6,081	1,176	8,937	11,439	8,889
2,284	1,368	224	4,054	784	5,958	7,626	5,926
914	549	90	1,621	313	2,383	3,950	2,370
3,360	2,016	448	8,288	1,792	11,648	14,448	11,312
2,520	1,512	336	6,216	1,344	8,736	10,836	8,484
1,680	1,008	224	4,144	896	5,824	7,224	5,656
672	403	90	1,657	258	2,329	2,889	2,262
1,232	784	224	5,152	1,560	7,392	8,448	6,440
493	312	90	2,061	624	2,957	3,380	2,600
560	336	168	3,751	1,736	5,097	6,425	4,465
224	134	67	1,500	694	2,028	2,570	1,785
896	582	224	1,747	851	3,491	4,000	2,833
448	291	112	873	426	1,746	2,000	1,416
1,906	1,344	336	6,832	1,792	10,192	11,276	8,922
577	403	100	2,050	538	3,058	3,390	2,678
1,250	806	40	2,661	1,290	4,153	5,281	3,557
625	403	20	1,330	645	2,072	2,645	1,783
2,520	2,128	392	4,368	1,176	8,162	8,946	7,378
1,218	1,023	188	2,100	564	3,925	4,305	3,546
775	504	168	2,352	1,109	3,628	4,672	3,234
412	269	45	1,250	591	1,950	2,460	1,620

children, instead of selling it to us to feed to factory-farmed livestock. Now that we are likely to have to spend more exports on ever more costly power, we are going to have to think in terms of more protein to the acre. The following table compares the dry matter of comfrey with that of the other high protein crops, to give a general picture before we consider them in terms of amino-acids.

PRODUCTION PER ACRE

	Dry Matter cwt.	Crude Protein lb.	Oil lb.	Carbo-hydrate lb.	Fibre lb.
50 tons per acre Bocking comfrey	124	3,808	336	5,500	1,680
10 cwt. per acre soya beans*	9	314	150	325	40
15 cwt. soya beans	13½	560	225	488	60
30 cwt. per acre Spring Tic beans	25½	830	42	1,479	40

* From *Feeds and Feeding* by Professor Frank B. Morrison. Morrison Publishing Co., Clinton, Iowa, 1959.

This table is concerned with two entirely different types of crop. The beans are concentrated, storeable and transportable all over the world; they are nitrogen fixing, cheap to sow and grow, and have protein of a vastly higher quality. Even with a 10 cwt. yield the soya bean production of unsaturated vegetable oil is of very great value in the human diet, for it is an oil seed, and the soya bean meal that is fed to pigs has had all but about the quantity of oil that is in Tic beans extracted to be used in making margarine and other food products.

Comfrey however has seven times as much protein as soya bean even when growing in climates which suit the standard commercial varieties, and about eight times the carbohydrate. There are processes under development for direct pelleting under pressure which can produce the equivalent to pig and dairy nuts for conservation through the winter as well as for use as a supplementary concentrate to go with high fibre foods for starch equivalent, or to balance high carbohydrate foods such as pig swill.

Just as our farming will have to alter when tractor fuel is four times its price in relation to industrial products, so when our food and that for our stock doubles in cost, we shall have to think again about our crops and even our economic conventions. Farmers are the kind of men who plant walnut trees, knowing that it will be fifteen years before they get any nuts with the finest harvest for their sons and grandsons, and beautiful timber for gunstocks and furniture in a hundred years. Business men and politicians are mentally incapable of thinking as far ahead as farmers who will have to feed us still whatever runs short because of the townsman's greed.

Let us consider just how good this leaf protein is going to be as *stockfeed*, for those who have eaten the product of the various extraction processes for converting various forage crops into human food seem to agree that though these may be excellent for the 'underdeveloped countries' they themselves prefer eggs, bacon, milk and steak. As China has found after farming without fertilizers for more than forty centuries, pork and eggs make a 'vegetarian' diet more nutritious and tasty. It is vastly easier to be a lacto-vegetarian than a vegan (one who eats no products of animal origin at all, not even honey), especially now that an egg is officially regarded as a 'vegetable' by vegetarians because of its value in the diet, rather like South Africa deciding that Japanese are 'Europeans' or 'Blankes'—officially White because of the importance of trade.

Leaf proteins were called 'low grade', while those in fish, meat and eggs were called 'high grade', before we knew that the difference depended on the proportion of which kinds of amino-acid are present in any food, for very few natural foods are without either protein or carbohydrate, and our digestions are designed for mixed eating.

Amino-acids are classified into 'essential' and 'non-essential' and they differ from minerals and vitamins in being non-storable, acting rather like a certain size of spanner that must be found at once, or the tractor cannot be started. As an example, the amino-acids in milk supplement those in cereals and make them digestible, so porridge or muesli and milk is a nutritionally sound meal, but only a glass of milk at supper time will do nothing to help balance tomorrow's breakfast.

A diet which contains a mixture of proteins can add up to enough to make most foods available. An example is gelatin, one of the most 'mucilaginous' of the proteins and the first to be isolated. Though gelatin has very little food value itself, the links of amino-acids which make up its long chains of proteins, include many of lysine, which is short in both vegetables and cereals.

According to the Cruzada Nacional Por-Enriquemiento de los Alimentos, two-thirds of the population of Mexico are on a bean-maize (corn) diet, which is lacking in three essential amino-acids— methionine, isoleucine and tryptophan. Señor K. Beldin, Treasurer of the Cruzada, appealed to the H.D.R.A. to find if comfrey contained all or any of these essentials in the diet for very large areas of Central and South America. Even quite small advances in medicine and sanitation have produced a population 'explosion', and the problem is increasing. It is not one of starvation but malnutrition for lack of the right balance of amino-acids. The Cruzada is producing a number of cheap diet supplements and their addition to the present daily fare, says Señor Beldin, 'produces almost miraculous results in fostering the physical and mental development of growing children, even those already stunted from lack of protein of adequate quality'.

So the H.D.R.A. asked nature some rather expensive questions, and on 4 July 1966 their analyst, Dr. A. H. Ward, carried out the first amino-acid analysis of comfrey. They sent him their dried Bocking No. 14 'Tea' because this is more comparable with other concentrated vegetable protein sources, and though it is expensive to dry in temperate climates this is easy in tropical sunlight, which is free even to the hungry of all colours.

The table shows the result, with comparative figures from 'Amino-Acid Proportions in Food Proteins compared to proportions Utilized in Rat Growth' by N. Racia, J. Heimann and A. R. Kemmerer of the Department of Agricultural Biochemistry, University of Arizona (Agricultural) in *Food Chemistry*, Vol. 4, No. 8, August 1965.

Comfrey tea made of leaves only, is shown to be a richer source of protein than the other substances in the table. Because funds are always limited and amino-acids cost about £6 for each one in an analysis, the tests were done for those which are short on a bean and maize diet, and lysine because this is also scarce among vegans by poverty, rather than choice. They were not testing blindly, for the fact that it is possible to feed pigs successfully on comfrey and cereals alone has long been known to growers.

TABLE OF COMPARATIVE ANALYSIS
Four Essential Amino-Acids in Dried Comfrey and Other Foods

	Total Protein per cent	Methionine per cent	Tryptophan per cent	Lysine per cent	Isoleucine per cent
Comfrey tea (Bocking 14)	34·6	0·58	0·64	1·41	1·15
Soybeans whole	34·9	0·51	0·53	2·41	2·05
Lima (Butter) beans, dried	21·34	0·31	0·18	1·25	1·28
Lentils	24·52	0·20	0·20	1·43	1·16
Split peas (yellow)	19·79	0·15	0·18	1·41	1·00
Brazil nuts	15·99	0·87	0·15	0·34	0·60
Cashew nuts	18·93	0·30	0·41	0·68	1·06
Walnuts	16·31	0·28	0·16	0·40	0·70
Fresh brussels sprouts	4·11	0·046	0·033	0·17	0·18
Cheddar cheese	24·65	0·66	0·30	1·97	1·54
Mexican cheese	26·80	0·65	0·30	2·10	1·78

This table does not suggest that comfrey tea, as drunk with milk and sugar in Britain, and with lemon juice or dried peppermint in the U.S.A., has this percentage of amino-acids. It was simply used as a source of dried comfrey to show the proportion of them there would be in a dried flour made from the foliage.

Of the three amino-acids missing in Mexico, comfrey has the tryptophan which our eyes need in greater quantity than our bodies, for some exhaustive experiments with guinea-pigs have shown that a shortage that will not show in the growth rate brings cataract earlier, which will have been noted among many tribes where the elderly are blind more often than in better fed countries.

Comfrey is a very good source of tryptophan, rather more than a third better than cashew nuts, the runners up, more than three times as good as lentils and more than twice as good as cheese. Lentils had slightly more lysine, split peas the same, while the cheeses were well ahead, as all proteins of animal origin can be expected to be, while the nuts were far behind. Though these are a common protein source among vegans in the West, they are rarely used in the East because of their cost compared with the cheaper legumes to those who must feed a family for a day on the price of a health food magazine.

Methionine is the most urgent lack in Mexico and among the people of the shanty towns of Central and South America, and comfrey is about as good a source as cheese, though Brazil nuts are ahead by two-thirds—but these are usually for export only. Lima beans and cheeses are superior on isoleucine, and nuts are far behind, as they are on lysine.

The full table of the concentrated foods shows comfrey tea (Bocking Mixture, leaf only) ahead of soya bean on tryptophan and methionine, but with this ideal, though tasteless and low-yielding legume the winner on every other amino-acid. It should be realized that the comfrey figure is for the very best dried leaf though the proportions of the amino-acids in the protein would still be the same. Though comfrey is about $12\frac{1}{2}$ per cent dry matter as cut, the vastly greater yield even at 50 tons an acre puts it far ahead as a bulk vegetable protein supplier.

Relatively few feeding trials have been carried out with comfrey, mainly because most research stations are concerned to establish low yields or to 'disprove claims', but the work of Hubert Heitman Jr. and Milton D. Miller, at the University of California, was based on the 103 ton an acre level crops at Davis. The following report is reproduced from their 'Plant Leaf Protein, with Emphasis on Comfrey' by permission of Dr. H. L. Knowles, the Principal of the Department of Agronomy.

'The crop does not make seed and is propagated vegetatively. Under California conditions, the best time to transplant root cuttings appears to be in the spring, just as good growing conditions begin.

'Yield records have been kept on two campus plots. One (the old plot) consisted of 21 plants planted for previous work in 1958. This plot was abandoned in 1963. The old plot contains rows 3 feet apart, and plants within the row spaced at 3 feet; the new plot also has rows 3 feet apart, but the plants within the row are spaced at 2 feet.

'Both plots were irrigated with 3 inches of water per irrigation about every two weeks or as called for by weather conditions. Four top dressed treatments of 1726 lb. per acre of elemental nitrogen (as ammonium nitrate) were applied. Plots were weeded during the growing season.

'Leaves were harvested by hand with a hedge clipper. Harvesting continued from April 26 until November 16. Early in the season the harvesting interval was 10 to 20 days, but from August on yields dropped and harvesting intervals became longer.

'Yield data are given in table 1 [quoted in the previous chapter, page 69]. The average crude protein content of the old stand increased from 20·9 per cent in 1958 to 25·4 per cent in 1967. Reasons may have been age, yield, nitrogen fertilization, or others. Over this nine-year period, the yield per acre of dry matter decreased from 12·0 to 9·4 American tons, indicating longevity. The yield results agree with those reported by others, including Doring (1958) and the crude protein level is about the same as that reported by Ikeda *et al* (1962) and Ziglinskaja (1957). The crude protein level is slightly higher than that found by Kozicka-Nowakowa and Sokolowa (1961).

Animal Studies

'The analyses of comfrey dry matter are given in table 2. The comfrey, from both plots and harvested in the spring of 1967, was dehydrated in a forage dryer. The relatively high level of crude protein and moderate level of crude fiber are noteworthy, but so is the high level (over 23 per cent) of ash. An initial crude palatability study was made utilizing two 150-pound hogs. They consumed reasonable quantities of feed containing as much as 40 per cent of dehydrated comfrey. Higher levels were not tested.

'A rat feeding trial was designed to study the value of comfrey protein. Purified rations were used containing approximately 10 per cent crude protein, and dehydrated comfrey contributed 0, 20 and 40 per cent to the three rations. Nitrogen and crude fiber contents were equalized using casein, comfrey and cellulose (table 3). Analyses of the control ration and comfrey are presented in table 2. Thirty 21-day old Sprague Dawley male rats were randomized into the three groups and fed *ad libitum* for 21 days in individual cages.

'The results of the rat trial are shown in table 4. Analysis of variance indicated the differences in gain and feed consumption were highly significant (P 0.01). On the 40 per cent comfrey ration all 10 rats lost weight continuously through the trial, but about 56 per cent of the weight loss occurred in the first 7 days. One rat on the 20 per cent comfrey ration lost weight continuously and succumbed on the sixth day. The difference in feed conversion between the control and 20 per cent comfrey rations was highly significant (P 0.01) and the 40 per cent comfrey ration failed to even maintain weight. Adjustment of gains to equal feed consumption (170·1 gm.) by covariance analysis indicated that differences between adjusted gains (58·3, 26·1 and −2·1 gm., respectively) were highly significant (P 0.01).

'Even when only half of the crude protein came from comfrey (the other half came from casein), there were drastic reductions in feed consumption (about 24 per cent), gain (about 62 per cent) and feed conversion (about 50 per cent). The palatability of comfrey for rats was apparently less than for swine as indicated by the preliminary trial with swine.

'The digestibility of comfrey was determined in a 3 × 3 Latin square design digestion trial, with rations also containing 0, 20, and 40 per cent dehydrated comfrey (rations in table 5; analysis of comfrey and control ration in table 2) and three pigs weighing initially about 80 lb. and finally about 140 lb. Collection periods were 9, 9 and 8 days, and feed consumption was limited to 4, 5 and 6 lb. in each of the three periods respectively. The results are summarized in table 6. The digestion coefficients indicate a calculated total digestible nutrient (TDN) content of 52·7 per cent for the comfrey and a digestible crude protein level of 12·1 per cent.

'Analyses of variance were calculated for the apparent co-efficients of digestibility of the organic components of the proxi-mate analysis for the three swine rations. In spite of the small number of observations, the differences between the rations were statistically significant for crude protein (P 0.05) and crude fibre (P 0.01). The differences in co-efficients for ether extract approached significance, but they lacked significance for the nitrogen-free extract (NFE).

'The analyses showed significant relationships between comfrey level of the rations and digestibility of crude protein and crude fibre (P 0.01) and ether extract (P 0.05). Regression co-efficients were positive for ether extract and crude fiber, indicating that the digestibility of their components was higher in comfrey than the control ration. The reverse was true for crude protein and NFE where the regression co-efficients were negative.

'The literature indicated that the comfrey used in these trials was somewhat representative of that reported by others, except that the ash content of the Davis-grown comfrey is high. Thus Siglinskaja (1957) and Ikeda *et al* (1962) reported ash levels 40 to 50 per cent lower while those reported by Kozicka-Nowakowa and Sokolowa (1961) varied from 10 to 40 per cent less. On the other hand, the levels of crude protein and crude fiber agree reasonably well except that the California-grown comfrey was somewhat higher in crude protein than that of the last cited workers. Their level of ether extract was also about 50 per cent greater even though it is relatively low in all samples. Patel *et al* (1962) reported a digestible crude protein level of 18·7 per cent with cattle, a level substantially above the value determined in our study with swine.

Summary

'The importance of protein in the diet indicates the need for more information on plant leaf protein. Quaker comfrey (*Symphytum peregrinum*) has been studied from the agronomic and animal standpoints.

'On the Davis Campus a plot yielded as high as 12 tons of dry matter per acre and after nine years still was yielding over 9 tons. The crude protein ran from 20 to 25 per cent or a yield of up to $2\frac{1}{2}$ tons crude protein per acre.

'In a study with rats, dehydrated comfrey at the 20 per cent level (supplying half of the protein in the ration) was not a satisfactory component of the diet, and at the 40 per cent level (only source of protein) it was completely unsatisfactory. A 3 × 3 factorial digestion trial with swine indicated that our sample of comfrey dry matter had digestible crude protein and TDN contents of 12·1 and 52·7 per cent respectively. The apparent digestibilities of crude protein and NFE were lower for comfrey than for the control ration as was the TDN content.'

Table 2. Proximate analyses of comfrey and control rations (dry matter basis)

| | Comfrey | | Control Rations | |
	Rat trial	Swine trial	Rat trial	Swine trial
		per cent		
Crude protein	26·0	24·4	10·3	17·6
Ether extract	2·4	3·4	3·9	1·2
Crude fiber	12·3	12·6	4·9	8·4
Nitrogen-free				
extract	35·7	35·9	77·4	67·1
Ash	23·6	23·7	3·5	5·7

Table 3. Rations, rat trial

| | Control | Comfrey | |
		20 per cent	40 per cent
		per cent	
Casein	11·0	5·5	—
Comfrey, dehydrated	—	20·1	40·3
Corn oil	5·0	5·0	5·0
Sucrose	71·4	60·1	48·7
Cellulose*	6·6	3·3	—
Salt mixture†	4·0	4·0	4·0
Vitamin mixture‡	2·0	2·0	2·0

* Solka-floc.
† Salt mixture P-H manufactured by Nutritional Biochemical Corporation, Cleveland, Ohio.
‡ Vitamin Diet Fortification Mixture manufactured by Nutritional Biochemical Corporation, Cleveland, Ohio.

Table 4. *Results, rat trial*
(21 days, 10 rats per group)

	Control	Comfrey	
		†20 per cent	40 per cent
Final weight, gm.	107·4	68·4	36·9
Initial weight, gm.	42·8	43·7	44·2
Gain, gm.	64·6[a]*	24·8[b]	−7·3[c]
Feed consumption, gm.	212·6[x]	161·9[y]	135·1[z]
Feed per unit gain	3·36[a]	6·77[b]	—

* Numbers on same line differ significantly from those with different superscripts a, b, c (P<0·01): x, y, z (P<0·05).
† One rat succumbed on the sixth day on this ration. Data based on nine rats fed the 20 per cent comfrey ration.

Table 5. *Rations,* * *swine digestion trial*

	Control	Comfrey	
		20 per cent	40 per cent
		pounds	
Ground barley	83		
Cottonseed meal (41% CP)	11		
Meat and bone meal (50% CP)	6		
Salt	0·5		
Control (above)		80	60
Ground, dehydrated comfrey		20	40

* Plus 1675 IU vitamin A and 90 IU vitamin D_2, per pound of ration.

Table 6. *Results of swine digestion trial*
(3 × 3 Latin square)

	Coefficients, apparent digestibility	
	Control ration	Comfrey*
	per cent	
Crude protein	73·7	49·6
Ether extract	26·5	80·3
Crude fiber	14·9	84·5
Nitrogen-free extract	83·2	66·5
Calculated total digestible nutrients (TDN, per cent)	70·8	52·7

* Calculated by difference between the control ration and the 20 and 40 per cent comfrey rations.

Pigs, poultry and human beings are all omnivorous, and though it is possible with skill enough to live on an all vegetable diet, pigs have few principles and without what used to be called 'the animal protein factor' they failed to thrive. This was not an amino-acid, but a vitamin which is present in such small traces that it is measured in nanograms per 100 grams—thousandths of a millionth of a gram—vitamin B12.

One of the comfrey growers in the 1954 Comfrey Race was Paul Weir, who was perfectly satisfied with his 22 ton an acre yield because it enabled him to rear what may have been Britain's first veganic pigs. At the time feeding stuffs were strictly rationed, and only those who had kept pigs before the 1939–45 War were allowed any meal at all. With his wife and his small son, he started small-holding in an old railway carriage, propped up on bricks in an awkward triangle of woodland with all the big trees felled by Canadian lumbermen who left the top and lop behind.

Fortunately it was near a Ministry of Food Depot, and from this Paul Weir was able to buy large quantities of condemned dates in boxes about four feet long, whose sides, plus secondhand corrugated iron and sawn up branches, built his piggeries. The dates, at incredibly low prices, plus comfrey, fed his pigs, and the woods were full of the stones that passed through undigested, and they are probably still there now the woodland is built on, after giving one young, keen couple a start on the land.

In theory his pigs should have been fed tinned snoek or over-age spam to supply the missing animal protein factor, but these went for better prices to pet food makers, together with the final horror that rationed Britain was spared—a consignment of tinned octopus in ink bought from Spain in 1943 for diplomatic reasons. In defiance of theory the pigs throve, for a pig as heavy as a man can easily take its entire bodily needs of B12 in about four pounds of fresh comfrey a day.

This applies also to chickens and to any animal which does not have the digestive bacteria to synthetize its own supply, like the ruminants such as cattle and sheep. From the work of Dr. Frank Wokes of the Vegetarian Nutritional Research Centre, it is now known that other bacteria in the digestive organs of earthworms also synthetize vitamin B12 and this is how free range poultry peck up their needs and why battery birds must have theirs added in fishmeal.

A number of plankton and seaweeds, of which laver (*Porphyra vulgaris*) is the best known, can also synthetize this vital vitamin, which depends on a trace of cobalt for its manufacture, and this is present in comfrey, the only land plant so far known to take it from the soil.

In 1959, a Mrs. Dorothy Johnson of New Zealand had strongly advocated eating comfrey root and leaf as a cure for asthma, and comfrey growers in many countries were flooded with enquiries as the press got hold of the idea. The H.D.R.A. had some dried leaf made into tablets for Mr. F. Newman Turner, M.B.N.O.A., M.N.I.M.H., N.D.O., N.D.A., who was Consultant to the Society of Medical Herbalists as well as President of the Association, to try on his patients.

As a famous vegetarian as well as a herbalist, he saw far more vegans than any doctor, and one of the advantages of years of experience in curing cattle is the habit of observing symptoms, as well as listening to what the patient says. One of the symptoms of B12 deficiency is a sore tongue, and though our bodies can store this and other vitamins for long periods, vegans who do not take sufficient care over their quite difficult diet often have sore tongues and inflammation round the eyes as their reserves run out. He happened to have several patients with both sore tongues and asthma and put them on comfrey tablets, which had no effect on the asthma, but cleared up the B12 deficiency symptoms instead.

So Mr. Newman Turner suggested that the H.D.R.A. should send a sample of their Bocking No. 4 flour to Dr. Ward for analysis for B12. By coincidence in that same summer, two other H.D.R.A. members, Mr. John Beck of Bradford and Mr. Geoffrey Wheeler of Bodmin, had discovered that six square inches a day of comfrey leaf would cure the symptoms of B12 deficiency in chinchillas. These squirrel-like and expensive animals, bred for fur, probably eat some insect in the wild state to provide their supply, and when they run short they eat their own droppings to

4

recycle the last of the vitamin. These two expert chinchilla breeders found that though their animals refused to eat leaves of anything of the cabbage tribe they enjoyed comfrey and stopped eating their droppings. Though B12 tablets can be bought these do not appear to agree with chinchillas and in winter it is easiest to feed them comfrey tablets, which they sit up and nibble like nuts.

As a matter of historic interest, Mr. Newman Turner's opinion, based on observations of his patients, was first expressed at the foundation meeting of the Vegetarian Nutritional Research Centre, and confirmed by the sample tested. The analysis was made by Dr. A. H. Ward of Aynsome Laboratories, Grange-over-Sands, Lancashire, Consulting Analyst to the H.D.R.A.: its laboratory number was Y649, dated 28 October, 1959; and the framed certificate was shown on the H.D.R.A. stand at the Royal Horticultural Society's Flower Show in November 1959. The amount present was 0·58 micrograms per 100 grams.

Traces of B12 have been found in turnips and lucerne in the U.S.A., but in isolated instances, suggesting chance leaf contamination by soil splashed up by rain. At the time it was believed that grazing animals passing B12 with their droppings, and sewage sludge were the only sources of the vitamin, but the work of Dr. Wokes shows that any soil with a healthy supply of earthworms has plenty of this vitamin both for splashing on to leaves, and for rooting pigs to take up in the soil they eat, which can also correct their mineral deficiencies. In 1959, however, the mystery was the presence of B12 in the main trial rows at Bocking, which had only been manured with deep litter poultry compost.

Dr. Lester Smith, the authority on 'Vitamin B12' (Methuen, 1960) spent nearly ten years trying to extract the vitamin from sewage sludge, which in theory contained an average of £50 worth in every ton, and an extraction process which would recycle it on the principle of chinchillas eating their droppings would have been cheaper than growing bacteria in penicillin waste developed by Messrs. Glaxo Ltd. Unfortunately he failed, and those who need concentrated B12 because they are suffering from liver damage, or other disabilities which make their bodies use the vitamin in-

efficiently, have to buy it expensively, unless it is prescribed on the
N.H.S. For pigs and poultry comfrey is cheaper than fishmeal or
B12 injections, or the liver extract for those whose digestions take
this up more easily.

Because of the leaf splashing idea, the H.D.R.A. carried out a
number of tests with the other comfrey flour they had in stock in
1959, only one of which, from Redhill, Surrey, was manured with
sewage sludge. Both in the first set of samples and the second from
the April and May cuts in 1960, the Redhill samples were not
remarkably higher than the others.

1959 B12 TESTS

	nanograms per gram
Chase Flour. Chertsey 1	7·8
Chase Flour. Chertsey 2	4·0
Bocking No. 4 Redhill	5·8
Bocking Mixture, Colchester	4·5
Bocking Mixture, Kenya	7·4
Comparison	
Dried Yeast	1·1

1960 B12 TESTS

	nanograms per gram
Bocking No. 2	4·9
Bocking No. 4	11·6
Bocking No. 14	4·4
Bocking No. 17	5·0
Bocking No. 4 (Redhill)	3·1

In 1961 experiments were tried at Bocking, to see if it would be
possible to increase the B12 content of comfrey by manuring with
sludge deliberately, using material supplied and analysed by the
Huyton-with-Roby Corporation.

1961 SLUDGE AND B12 TRIAL

	nanograms per gram
Huyton-with-Roby Sludge	81·0
Milwaukee Sludge (From 'Vitamin B12' by Dr. Lester Smith)	71·0
Best Dried Comfrey	11·4
Average Dried Comfrey	5·6

The following tables give results and comparative yields from sludge with poultry droppings as a comparison:

Replicated Plots Bocking No. 16	nanograms per gram
Cut 22 April Sludge	0·35
Cut 22 April Poultry	0·37
Cut 5 June Sludge	1·58
Cut 5 June Poultry	1·78
Cut 27 September Sludge	10·20
Cut 27 September Poultry	4·70

It will be noted that the level of the B12 from both sludge and poultry manure went up steadily through the season. However, shortage of funds to pay for analysis at £6 per sample prevented further work at the time. The only way to measure B12 in the 1960s was to grow bacteria on it and measure their increase, which was costly. Now there is a method involving expensive apparatus which is more accurate but more costly than ever.

During the summer of 1960 Dr. Frank Wokes and his colleagues rooted comfrey stems supplied from the Bocking trial ground with a plant hormone and after the bases of the stems had sealed themselves to avoid any possibility of suction through the cut sap channels (florists dye cut flowers of chrysanthemum 'Esther Read' by this suction) the new roots were immersed in a B12 solution.

In the words of Dr. Wokes: 'A Comfrey plant has its new roots immersed in 2 fluid oz. of water containing 40 milligrams of B12. After 24 hours it was taken out, rinsed and immersed for 24 hours in water containing no B12, then dried and examined. A second Comfrey plant followed the first in the B12 and then the water and was also dried and examined. After the 48 hours 11 of the 40 milligrams of B12 had passed into the two plants.' The experiment was repeated several times, and I saw the red B12 solution glowing through the leaf veins under Dr. Wokes' microscope which he brought to Bocking with some of his rooted stems. *Other plants were rooted in the same way and failed to take the B12 out of the solution.* The results of this classic experiment were published by the Vegetarian Nutritional Research Centre.

The bacterium which is normally used for testing B12 is *Lactobacillus leichmanii* which is easy to keep as a culture in a commercial laboratory ready for any test that may be required. Dr. Wokes prefers another species, *Ochormonas malhamensis,* which is awkward to keep in a laboratory, but in his opinion, rather more accurate. The problem is that vitamin B12 is always found with a number of 'analogues', which are substances near it, but not quite the same, and the question is 'which bacterium has a digestion nearest to a human one, in terms of the selection of analogues it makes'.

In theory, it would take 3 to 4 lb. of fresh comfrey or 7 oz. of flour to supply all the B12 an adult needs in a day. Yet the vegans whose sore tongues Mr. Newman Turner cured took only 12 tablets a day, when in theory they should have eaten nearer 300. The evidence is that comfrey must fit the human digestion rather better than it does that of bacteria. Work continues in this field because of the long term value of a vegetable source of Vitamin B12 for those who cannot afford liver, eggs, milk and all the animal products (liver is the richest source) supplying B12 for well-fed Western men today. But not perhaps tomorrow.

5. The cultivation and conservation of comfrey

Comfrey requires a deep soil, not necessarily a good one, but deep, and it will always fail on thin soils over rock, including chalk, and on peat. A minimum depth of four feet is desirable, and on sandy soils with a hard pan, a subsoil plough should be used, for comfrey drives its roots deep bringing up calcium, phosphorus and potash, not to mention trace elements, to recapture leached-out plant foods already over the 'horizon' so far as normal crops are concerned, by going down further than anything but sizeable trees.

Unlike lucerne (alfalfa in the U.S.A.), it is not a legume, with nitrogen-fixing bacteria in its roots, but a member of the order *Boraginaceae* to which that powerful border plant Anchusa also belongs. So its nitrogen must be supplied in manure, and also by the free living nitrogen-fixing bacteria which take their energy from humus. Because comfrey is growing faster than any other fodder crop, it needs nitrogen quickly, and this is why there has never been a large crop on a farm or in a garden fed with compost —the nitrogen is available too slowly. Neither has there ever been a good one in grass, because this takes up nitrogen in competition with the comfrey, exactly as grassing down an orchard enables tree growth to be *slowed down* and fruiting improved by mowing and management.

A comfrey plot lives as long as an orchard. Its site should be selected with the same care. It needs to be near the farm buildings or where it is to be fed, because even 50 tons an acre cut from four to six times a summer means bulk to carry. On any farm it is usual to plant a small plot for a trial and increase it later, but small plots of anything get neglected if they are at all awkward to handle, so the site should be the small corner which so easily becomes a rubbish dump, provided it is sunny and well drained. Where a large field is to be put down, choose somewhere open and sunny and convenient to get machinery into bearing in mind that the crop must be carted off it, and not grazed. Aim at long runs for the mower, the chopper blower or whatever mechanized forage harvester you are using.

A frost hollow does not matter because comfrey will take far more cold than we get in Britain. It yields more in tropical countries because of the longer cutting season, not because it is not hardy. It will take flooding, but this can be awkward because of the difficulty of getting on the land early to give it a spring clean up. Always avoid a position under trees for plots large or small, because these will rob it of sunlight and moisture, while the more you manure the comfrey the greedier the tree or hedge roots can become.

Another reason for siting near the stock accommodation is for easy manure haulage. The ideal manure is deep litter compost, and the houses can be cleaned to suit the most convenient date for re-starting the litter, ideally between November and March, with March the ideal month, when a cultivator between the rows and a three-inch thick coat of litter will produce heavy yields with no trouble from weeds. Choose the site for easy spreading with a tractor and fore loader. Comfrey will always take its manuring raw and crude, and farm slurry can be sprayed or spread direct on the crop through the spring and summer, but this is wasteful in winter, though it is tough enough to take the water-logging where the material must be disposed of all the year round. A comfrey field which is used for daily cuts through the season is never all clear at once, so slurry needs an irrigation system to get it into the uncut crop, or enough cleared in a week to spread over.

Preparing the Ground

The ideal planting months for comfrey are March, April and May, with September as second choice, for this allows time for the plants to become established before they go dormant for the winter. September planting has the advantage that the land can be summer fallowed to kill the weeds, with special reference to couch grass (*Agropyrum repens*) and other perennials. Three or four rotary cultivations at 3 to 4 week intervals in dry weather will kill out couch and a great deal of thistle.

Those who have pigs can use these as ground clearers by tethering dry sows and boars where the docks and nettles are thickest, feeding only enough pignuts to keep their snouts down, for unrung pigs are splendid weedkillers. In areas where it is desired to kill out wild comfrey, or when a poorly-sited crop or a change in farm policy demands that a plot should be destroyed, then pigs are the cheapest answer. They are extremely fond of comfrey root, which they hunt by scent like truffles, and in three months they will leave no trace of the crop. So fence the plot well to keep the pigs on it, if it is a cleared rubbish patch full of weeds, then afterwards the fencing will keep it safe from stock.

If there is plenty of manure available, plough in up to 20 tons an acre, or a good heavy dressing. Anyone who has battery poultry manure free for the fetching can plough in this instead. The problem of this by-product of factory farming is that it becomes a kind of silage, arresting its own decay by the exclusion of air, but under a comfrey bed in the autumn, with about 2 tons an acre of lime on the surface harrowed in before planting in spring, it will become slowly available. The deep litter poultry-keeper who is turning over to comfrey feeding to save protein costs has no problem: he can simply use a clearing of one of his houses as a dressing before planting.

Spent mushroom compost is a useful source of humus for starting comfrey on poor soil. This is a mixture of straw, horse manure, dried blood and small chalk lumps, plus some casing soil. Most of its energy and nitrogen has gone to feed the mushroom crop, but there is quite a good supply left, and the chalk has the asset of going on safely at the same time as the manure and lasting for many years. Slaked lime consists of millions of dust-fine particles with perhaps half a square mile of surface area in every 56 lb. bag, which provides plenty of working space for root secretions to take up the calcium, and for the correction of acidity by chemical reaction. The lumps in mushroom compost have a relatively tiny surface area and so last for ages. Ground chalk or ground limestone are rather better than slaked lime, but as always on a farm, it is a question of what is available locally at minimum haulage cost.

Planting Comfrey

The standard spacing for farm plots of comfrey is three feet apart each way, or 4,840 to the acre, while those who have rechristened 'The Twenty Acre Piece' the 'Eight-point-nought-nine-three-seven Hectare Field', can make it three feet three and a bit inches, or a metre apart each way, which means 10,000 plants to the hectare.

The reason for this wide spacing is because a comfrey plant which is four years old and good for six more years of productive youth can be eighteen inches across, and though the plants look wide through their first two years, this leaves room for between row cultivations to keep down the weeds which are at their worst in the early years. The reason for equal distances between plants and rows is to allow for 'cross blocking' as with sugar beet, which is putting the cultivator, or rotary hoe, such as a Howard, or Merry-tiller on a smaller scale, first between the rows and then between the plants, crossing the field in both directions.

Because of this need, it is important to space the plants accurately, which is best done with a cabbage marker, a tool with large wide wheels which can be set to varied distances for towing behind a horse or tractor (some horses were very good at this job) crossing the field both ways, for planting where the lines cross each other. It is a task like rather wide cabbage planting and a transplanting machine can be used.

The essential is to get the offsets with their growing points upwards and *below* the surface, for if they stand out of the ground they can dry out and die very easily—the only time the crop is really at risk. If the growing points are between half an inch and an inch below the soil surface, it is possible to firm the new plants in with a flat roller, or even a Cambridge one. (Gardeners should turn ahead to their chapter for small scale directions.)

When the crop is well up, choose the weather and put the hoes through it to get a kill of the weeds, especially the grass, and two or three good hoeings in the first year will be repaid through the twenty-year life of the crop. About June or July the plants will throw up flower stems among their leaves, and this is when it pays to mow for the first time, setting the knife to cut about two inches above the ground. Flowering early weakens the crop, and cutting puts its strength into building up bigger plants for next season.

If the plants have done well, a first cut is possible in September as a trial trip, cutting as always at two inches from the ground, but do not cut later than the end of the month, to give time for the plants to recover before the winter.

Cutting and Cultivation

The crop will still need row crop cultivation between cuts in the second year, but once it is clean, those who have deep litter compost can spread it to hold down the weeds and feed the crop. Cutting for stock feed should start in April and although on a small scale a scythe used to be used, a rough grass mower like an Allen is ideal for the daily cuts to feed pigs, poultry and horses.

The first daily cuts will cross the plot from side to side in perhaps a fortnight, the first needing many rows to supply the demand which perhaps ten will fill when the crop has gathered speed. Go back to the beginning again, and aim to cross the plot every six weeks, which is about the optimum cutting interval. So long as the stock is fed and makes a profit there is no need to worry about record making, so if it 'gets away' in a warm wet summer, and runs up to four or five feet of flowering stem, mow it and let it lie to rot down, if you have no grazing stock to eat it, so that you will have young high protein leaves for pigs and poultry.

The third year should see the crop in full production, and the plants should be meeting in the rows on good land, or with ample feeding. Aim to have the mower and buck rake, or whatever picks up the crop, always in the same place and in order so that it can go out and do its daily job with minimum trouble. It is on the job which you do every day that minutes add up to half hours. The only chance the weeds should get to grow is between cuts, so any cultivation should be shallow and fitted in then. As the plot matures the weed seeds will have germinated and there will be fewer and fewer left to give trouble.

This is a reason why deep litter compost is best, because the hens will have pecked any weed seeds out of the straw. Straw deep litter compost is ideal because it breaks down completely to good humus on the surface, while shavings can be excellent, provided they do not contain too many wood ends. These have exactly the same problem as the lime lumps—they present a too small working surface for the bacteria which run the deep litter system, notably *Hutchinson's spirochaete*, the best hard cellulose cracker in the trade. This creature, which has lived in farmyards ever since Neolithic farmers were buried in round barrows on their broad acres, prefers the ammonium carbonate in urine, which is in the dab of white on every poultry dropping. If it cannot complete the job before the house is cleared, the woodends stay on the surface and accumulate, but if they are turned under they will rob the soil of nitrogen at the expense of the crop. The following table shows the analysis of deep litter composts with other manures for comparison.

Full Analysis	Water per cent	N. per cent	P. per cent	K. per cent	Cal. per cent	C.-N. Ratio
F.Y.M. Rothamsted average	76·0	0·64	0·23	0·32	—	14–1
Straw and sludge compost	46·50	0·80	0·55	0·15	1·5	10–1
Fresh poultry manure	76·0	1·66	0·91	0·48	—	—
Straw deep litter	50·2	0·93	1·63	0·65	—	12–1
Hardwood shavings litter	39·2	1·0	1·98	1·0	—	9·2–1
Softwood shavings litter	20·4	2·25	2·5	1·5	3·7	9–1
Rhodesian shavings	13·4	1·9	2·75	1·6	4·5	11–1
Broiler litter shavings	27·2	2·1	2·15	1·55	—	13–1
Peat litter	17·7	4·4	1·9	1·9	2·2	—
Hop manure	—	0·8	1·5	1·0	—	—
Grassland fertilizer	—	8·0	7·75	3·37	—	—

Fertilizer prices go higher and higher, so none are given, but the man who was using the soft wood shavings, from a factory making fishboxes, which he got as free return loads from his nearest town, was in 1956 getting a manure worth about £8 a ton on unit valuation. No one would pay him that much for it, but a comfrey bed would earn him far more in saved feed, if he kept his manure on the farm, like his father, grandfather and great-grandfather had before him.

It will be noticed that the shavings deep litter samples are much higher in potash than the others, because this plant food is released from the broken down wood. The peat is high in nitrogen because the bacteria cannot break up the litter for exactly the same reason that old boots take longest of anything to decay on a compost heap—they are preserved by their tannin. The peat tends to accumulate on the surface of the plot, and of course it is an expensive litter. Those who use it for special reasons should be prepared to drag off any surplus in winter, and use it elsewhere as they can accumulated woodends.

Slurry manuring with a small tractor-drawn tanker, or an over-head spray line, has the disadvantage of not providing a weed suppressing mulch, but it is possible to use up very much more manure from 'cowtel' or 'feedlot' farming, or merely cow stall and piggery washings. Liming in the autumn or spring, using slaked lime to wash in quickly, is desirable when slurry is used, for this can make the soil steadily more acid, which a shavings deep litter never will, with the steady release of calcium from the wood.

Those who are fortunate enough to be near a sewage works using the heated digestion process, and distributing its sludge to farmers, can use this tar-like, odourless liquid thankfully. A good tanker sludge should be 4·4 per cent dry matter, of which 6·8 per cent will be nitrogen, 4·7 per cent phosphorus and 0·15 per cent potash, and this dry matter should be not more than 900 p.p.m. lead, or whatever the current Ministry of Agriculture safety standard is.

If a sludge is used, this should be applied with a rain gun irrigator supplied through a tractor or tanker mounted pump, for the minimum sized tankers used by local authorities hold 750 gallons. Most are 2,000 gallons and upwards, and a comfrey plot is too soft to take vehicles this size. Any liquid spraying should ideally be on fresh cut comfrey, or with up to a week's growth on it, so there will be no problem of blocking the leaf pores and damaging the crop, though this is a risk only in dry weather. The comfrey plot at Redhill Aerodrome was tanker-sludge fed for many years.

Increasing Comfrey

As comfrey plants age they die out in the middle, looking rather like coral atolls or moon craters. This is because instead of making a main tap root like a tree out of woody material which lives about 80 years in the case of an oak, comfrey grows soft ones like horse radish. Only the layers immediately under the bark of a tree root take part in the two-way traffic of minerals and water upwards and sugars for energy material, and waste products such as carbonic acids for excretion, downwards.

Tree roots stay alive with hemicellulose and lignins in long strong fibres like those of wood for they must support the weight and leverage of the timber above. Those of root vegetables have also a two-way traffic layer on the outside, but in the centre they have stored starches and proteins ready to provide energy and materials for the towering flower and seedhead which these biennials thrust up in their second season. The ideal beetroot (from the beet's point of view) is a bolter.

Comfrey roots come between the two. They have no super-structure to support, so have no need to grow wood, locking up plant foods till only fire or slow decay can release them, like potash in a tree trunk. They are not temporary constructions like those of a carrot or parsnip, but their roots must be built on the same plan, for every autumn in a temperate climate comfrey leaves return their minerals and starches to store to give next season's crop a flying start. It is for this reason that most growers make a final cut in early October or equivalent in their latitude and leave the last three weeks of growth to increase the size of the first cut in spring when they need the food more urgently.

The 'crater effect' on ageing comfrey plants comes from the main roots wearing out and rotting off, just as the root hairs are dying and decaying in about 3 to 4 days. The normal routine as the plot ages is to walk along the rows with a hand fork after the April or May cut, dig up any of the outer crater rim that has extended far enough to interfere with row crop cultivation, and replant the pieces in empty middles, making sure that the growing points are well below the surface. The fungi which break down the worn-out roots do not attack living comfrey.

Most comfrey beds start with a small area on trial and if the crop proves satisfactory under local conditions and farm economics, the owner will wish to increase it. This is best left until the third spring after planting to make certain that the crop has been allowed the minimum time to become established, and will yield enough to pay when kept clean, cut and fed.

In March or April, drive a sharp spade through the main root of each plant about three inches below the surface, and lift off the severed crowns. Divide these with a sharp knife into sections, each with a growing point and a section of the thick, brown root, doing the job on a sack to avoid allowing fragments of root to fall on the soil, where they will be trodden in and grow. Though comfrey rarely sets seed, every tiny piece of root will become a new plant, so the sack should be emptied into the pig trough, or, on a garden scale, dumped in the dustbin.

The many thriving plants of varied comfrey beside the lanes of Britain and Europe date from the 1880–90 comfrey boom, when gypsies knew that a double handful of comfrey root a day would restore the most miserable specimen of horse to glossy-coated health, despite filed teeth and other defects, for long enough for them to get well away from the area. By tradition they used *S. officinale*, but cultivated comfrey was just as good, in fact it had rather higher allantoin, and was more easily gathered. Spilt fragments from this 'health food' for horses explain why comfrey is so common round good roadside caravan sites.

On a large scale, harrow the field after the crowns have been removed, or spade back the soil over the cut surfaces on a small plot. Then after six weeks new growing points will appear, and if the operation is carried out in early April, there will be a cut of comfrey ready in July. The crowns will cut up to provide 4 to 8 new plants as originally bought, each ready to plant at the same spacing on ground prepared in the same way. The original plot misses two cuts but the following year it will be as good as ever.

This system of increase is by far the best because the parent planting stays at the original spacing. If it were dug up completely the yield would go back to that of a new planting, and the cut root fragments could grow up between the rows. If the need is to move a plot entirely, or to destroy one that is dying after perhaps twenty-five years production, then whole plants should be dug up with as much root as possible.

First cut off the tops to make as many plants with growing points as possible, and then slice up the roots into 2 to 3 inch long

PROPAGATION AND MODE OF CUTTING PRICKLY
COMFREY SETS

ROOT-SET—This is a section cut off a tap root, and if placed in soil with the small end downwards will throw a large number of heads, which do not always bloom the first year, but yield a large crop. Another plan is to place the sets in a damp sack kept warm and moist in the dark; shoots are thrown out, and when ½-inch long the sets may be planted, and the shoots will bloom the first year.

CROWN-SET—This is taken from the root of the plant near the surface of the ground, and the smallest piece forms a crown-set that blooms at once.

ROOT-SET   CROWN-SET

Fig. 8 Root cutting and crown reproduced from Thomas Christy's *Forage Crops*. The crown on the right has about the maximum cut surface and both are natural size, but are small for successful propagation. Large pieces are better.

sections. These are for planting as root cutting for maximum increase. Take out a furrow two inches deep along a line and lay the root sections flat along it about an inch apart, so their upper cut surfaces will grow new shoots while they root from their lower ends. There is no need to take trouble to keep the root cuttings the same way up that they grew, as with *Phlox paniculata*, *Morisia hypogaea*, *Papaver orientale* and other plants propagated in this way. Comfrey is so much stronger that the cuttings pull themselves upright if they go flat on the trench bottom.

This method produces far more plants, and with an old plot, it gives a chance to select the best, either according to the descriptions in Chapter 3 or from experience. Root cuttings planted in the spring should be ready for their permanent positions by the following spring, or by the autumn if the bed has been well manured, which means fewer really small plants. The root cutting rows should be a foot apart, and they will need at least one hoeing to keep the weeds down between the rows, before they are covered with deep-litter compost for maximum growth. The root cutting bed will become full of broken root ends which will grow, and therefore those who wish to increase Bocking No. 4, No. 14 or any other variety should keep each to its own root cutting bed, or kill out between plantings.

Killing Comfrey

The desperate appeal from the Irish press letter writer in the 1890s, for someone to tell him how to get rid of comfrey, still echoes from those who grow this crop badly. Those who grow it well no more want to get rid of it than good fruit growers wish to destroy established orchards, although neglected trees grown by a man who knows nothing about apples are also quite difficult to get rid of.

The simplest way is for the farmer who wishes to convert his comfrey bed back to pasture. He should plough and cultivate in December or January, the only time of year when comfrey plants are damaged by machinery, and sow to a four-year ley in the spring. The grass will slowly destroy his comfrey, though a few fragments will persist in the hedge bank as they do from the 1890s.

The best way to destroy elderly comfrey is, as stated earlier, to turn on the pigs, ideally tethering dry sows or the boar on the worst places, and they should clear the plot in six months. In Kenya and Rhodesia and Zambia, where comfrey plants wear out fast with the constant growth cycles, lasting about twelve years, the favourite method is to run chickens on the old plot after removing the crowns for a new planting, in the *dry season*. The birds peck up every blade of leaf as fast as it appears and the roots die out before the rains. Both the pig and poultry methods were found by growers who did not *want* to kill their comfrey, and it should be said that the chicken answer is for tropical countries only.

Ploughing and harrowing in summer should never be used to try to kill comfrey, and rotavation is still worse. All these often-tried answers merely spread the broken roots wider and mean thousands of small plants which grow into tall strong perennial weeds in arable land. Grass is always the worst weed in comfrey and in time it will kill the remains of the crop. In a lawn, however, it can persist, because it withstands mowing as well as it does cutting.

On a garden or plot scale comfrey can be easily killed with sodium chlorate. Cut through the crowns about an inch below the ground and spread the white crystals on the creamy cut surface of the root. This will soak down the sap channels and should kill out the roots completely as it will those of a tree stump. The 1976 difficulty is that sodium chlorate is used to make an explosive by the I.R.A. so is therefore unobtainable.

A better and safer chemical killer is ammonium sulphamate, which was formerly used for fireproofing railway sleeper carriage curtains. These are now washed only very rarely, and dipped in the ammonium sulphamate solution afterwards, so tons of this chemical are now available. Roughly speaking it is sulphate of ammonia 'made crooked', and the greedier a weed is for nitrogen the more it takes and the harder it falls. Though the chemical is expensive, it has the great advantage of becoming sulphate of ammonia in about six weeks, and washing harmlessly from the soil.

Mix up a solution of 1 lb. in a gallon of water and put this on with a rosed can over 100 square feet, that is a square ten feet each way. This is for killing out the mess of small broken roots that attempting to kill by summer cultivation will bring. If the bed is a normal one, with plants at intervals, cut them first, wait till growth has started again, say a week, and then water the clumps carefully, giving them about a quart of the solution each, but of course they vary in size—if they are eighteen inches across they take more, but if they are growing as well as this it is cheaper to learn how to use the crop properly.

Ammonium sulphamate should only be put on during the spring and summer. The first week in September is about the latest date for using it in Britain, for if it is watered on in winter when the roots are not feeding you will waste this expensive but safe and effective weedkiller. It kills by bad diet, like poisoning a rat with a diet of white bread, but more quickly, and in six weeks the land can be sown or planted again. The test is when there is a rapid growth on the cleared ground of chickweed and groundsel from suppressed seeds. This killer is also effective for horse radish, equisetum (horsetail), convolvulus and all perennial weeds.

Comfrey Conservation—Silage

The major problem of comfrey is to conserve its summer bulk for winter keep, and in Kenya and other countries with an equal day length, to preserve the heavy rainy season cuts for the dry period when the yield dips. The difficulty is that it has so much protein in relation to carbohydrate that preservation using lactic acid fermentation by added sugars, such as molasses, is not easy, with a crop which has a high moisture content.

Twenty-four-hour wilting is advised to bring the cut down by 30 to 50 per cent of the water content, not only to save drainage in the silo, but to avoid carting water from the field. The N.A.A.S. advise that two gallons of molasses mixed with a further two of water is the minimum; three gallons rather better to make sure of a good lactic acid fermentation and the fall in pH value after heating that keeps the crop in a state of arrested decay. It is not the purpose of this book to deal with silage-making when the process is fully described in standard textbooks, but the key to the process is the fermentation of carbohydrates, and this is why legume cereal mixtures and green maize, among crops grown for this method of preservation, require no added molasses. Comfrey, with the protein higher than any, but low in carbohydrates, needs the addition; if too little is added the proteins will not be preserved and their decay will make the whole product ill-smelling and distasteful to stock, apart from lost nutritional value. In this case the blame lies with bad silage-making, not the crop.

The silo should be filled loosely and the first four feet should go in totally unconsolidated and allowed to warm to blood heat before the rest of the crop is filled in. There should be some drainage provision as there will be a loss of liquid, but not on any great scale if the crop is well wilted. There is no need to chaff it, as unlike other stemmy materials the fibre is low and the stems break up; 25 tons of maize, as an example, contain over a third more fibre than 50 tons of comfrey. Nor is there any great range of analysis figures giving sufficient comparisons to show if there were better or worse comfrey silage makers. The one we have by this method shows 17·69 per cent fibre, 17·7 per cent crude protein, 14·37 per cent digestible protein, and 14·69 per cent ash.

Dr. Stephen J. Watson, in his experiments with silage at the I.C.I. Jealotts Hill Research Station, made some by the A.I.V. process, using *Symphytum peregrinum* so far as is known. His analysis is as follows, with other materials calculated on the same drymatter basis from the Ministry of Agriculture Bulletin 48:

	Moisture per cent	Crude Protein per cent	Ether extract (oil) per cent	Nitrogen-free extract (carbo-hydrate) per cent	Fibre per cent	Ash per cent
Comfrey silage	79·20	22·42	2·72	42·68	19·85	12·35
Maize (green) silage	81·05	8·65	4·32	78·60	40·60	7·60
Kale silage	84·10	12·60	3·14	45·40	23·10	15·60
Cereal-legume-silage	72·70	12·45	4·38	45·60	29·30	8·05
Good grass silage	79·00	18·10	4·76	47·20	20·40	10·00

To quote their report: 'The Prickly Comfrey made a good silage of high protein content. The breakdown of proteins was not excessive and the material was eaten readily. According to the textbook, prickly Comfrey silage is usually disagreeable in odour.'

The reason for this last remark is because all the textbooks are quoting from the remote past, before either molasses or A.I.V. silage-making were discovered. In agriculture, the figures that men use live after them, their practical farming background is oft interred with their bones. The A.I.V. process, which consists of adding a solution of acids to the material and by-passing the need for lactic acid fermentation, is more popular on the Continent than in Britain because of the precautions necessary in handling sulphuric acid and hydrochloric acid. It is patented and called after its inventor, the Finnish investigator, A. I. Virtanen.

The easiest way of using unwanted summer cuts of comfrey to help winter keep is as an addition where silage is already made. Up to 25 per cent of the fill with grass, cereal-legume mixture or maize can be comfrey, either chaffed or as cut, and the result is excellent, with no special precautions or variation in technique. The carbohydrates in the crop balance the excess protein and the finished product is balanced at a higher level of quality.

The late Mr. J. W. Hobbs of the Great Glen Cattle Ranch, Fort William, used to put the production of his $1\frac{1}{2}$-acre comfrey bed through a chopper blower and mix it with 'mashlum', which is Scots for oats and vetches cut at the milky high carbohydrate stage, and made silage with 14·57 per cent protein including comfrey, and 10·08 per cent for mashlum alone, according to the North of Scotland Agricultural College analysis.

Mr. J. McInnes at Nakuru used half comfrey and half Napier Fodder stacked in a normal 'pit' silo, with high banked soil sides and end, concrete lined. The effluent from comfrey silage is very rich in potassium and therefore should be run into a slurry tank, or distributed straight back on the land. He secured 18 to 20 per cent protein silage which is excellent by African standards, making it possible to replace concentrates in the dry season on the same scale as the green crop did through the rains.

Drying Comfrey Leaf

Dried comfrey is far too expensive to feed to cattle or pigs, for dry leaves are worth about £50 per cwt., and at £1,000 a ton for medicinal purposes, fish or soya bean meal is a far cheaper source of protein. The reason for this high price is the difficulty and high labour cost of drying.

At the moment the demand is supplied by peasants in Yugoslavia and Hungary who gather wild *S. officinale* and sun dry it for herbalists. Cultivated comfrey is richer in allantoin and produces a far nicer tea for drinking, for flavour, and medicinal value than the rather musty and variable product imported from Europe which contains a great deal of stem as well as wire and other foreign matter.

Comfrey has thick stems and midribs which hold in both the moisture and the protein, and can seal some of the moisture inside. Therefore the only satisfactory way of drying for the tea trade, is to grow it to the 'fountain of leaves stage', before it has inch-thick solid stems, and either pick the leaves by hand or mow and sort them out, discarding the stems. One way of handling the crop is to spread these leaves on inch mesh wire netting supported at a convenient height off the ground to allow free air circulation all round. When the leaves have wilted flabby, after about 48 hours, they are transferred to perforated zinc-bottomed drawers to slide into a cabinet dryer with an electric convector heater below, dried crisp and then broken down by rubbing through a sieve for packeting in polythene bags.

The late Mrs. P. B. Greer tried a number of drying methods, including a Nissen hut with a four-foot fan in the end, and found that all these obvious engineering answers failed. A basic problem is that too much heat can coagulate the gummy proteins like egg white and prevent the escape of further moisture, apart from the fact that if the drying temperature goes much over 180°F the allantoin breaks down and the medicinal value is lost. If the tea is to be green, attractive and tasty, it must be dried like any other herb, and faster than tobacco.

There is a big demand for comfrey tea, and though it has been dried in Rhodesian tobacco barns, the fundamental difficulty is the hand labour. Mr. P. Bowen-Colthurst, Mrs. Greer's nephew who carries on the business, has the midribs snipped out of the picked leaves and spread separately in a thin layer on the bottoms of cardboard flower boxes which are slid into racks in a polythene covered drying barn. The midribs are milled, but the leaf is rubbed through sieves and packed in polythene bags, which are always used for tea because the quantity of sodium and magnesium salts in comfrey makes it take up moisture from the air. It is not possible to make more than about eight hundredweight of the tea in a year at Layer-de-la-Haye and this all sells at a price that pays for the hand labour.

At Canby, Oregon, Mr. Chuck Peters has been drying comfrey for medicinal purposes and has devised a butane gas powered portable dryer to take out into the fields, and also a version of the barn hay drier with a belt moving the cut foliage slowly over natural gas heated air. The product, however, still has the drawback that the leaf dries but the stems stay wet. There is scope for invention in this field with a constantly increasing demand from health food shops. For the awkward fact about the medicinal value of comfrey is that though it cannot be established by medical research in any country so far because of its herbal connections, it exists. Those whom it has helped recommend it, and they need a supply for the winter when their plants are dormant. In the U.S.A., with no N.H.S., the alternative to 'folk medicine' can be bankruptcy, so experiments continue.

Comfrey Flour

If comfrey foliage goes through a shredder it can be dried in an ordinary drier as at Southery, and there is rather more allantoin in the stems than in the leaf. An ordinary compost shredder can be used and a batch or continuous process drier, but at the low temperature that tea needs if it is dried for medicinal purposes. No one should buy any mechanical device for drying comfrey, or sell one, until they have seen an analysis of the product, and seen a batch of foliage go through successfully. The gummy proteins of comfrey have beaten many an inventor.

Comfrey root is more easily dried, but this must be washed and cut up by hand. Though the roots do not contain the gummy proteins, they vary in thickness from about a quarter inch to two and a half inches, so must be reduced to roughly the same size to avoid the problem of the small ones drying before the large. The allantoin is present in the roots in winter, and dried comfrey root is also used by herbalists, but it is very little easier than leaf.

Roof Top Hay

This method was invented by Mr. E. V. Stephenson to dry small quantities of comfrey hay to feed in winter to his permanent 'staff' of stallions, trainer horses, hunters and his own brood mares. When there was surplus comfrey he had it thrown on to the sloping corrugated iron roofs of the loose boxes, to be taken down again when it had finally dried despite the rain in a Yorkshire summer.

One of the Holbrook Young Farmers' Club boys had the bright idea of using the football goal netting in summer to hold their hay on the roof, and this was quite effective. The principle of this simple system is that the black bitumen-painted corrugated iron roof slope gets very hot with the sun, and rain runs off under the crop along the corrugations. With a net made of nylon thick enough and with large enough meshes to hold the hay down in a windy summer, large quantities can be dried with little trouble, but in batches which must stay on the roof for a week, the leaves go black before the stems dry. As the basic variation of the Stephenson Strain is Bocking No. 14, Mr. Stephenson dried better hay on this system than growers with the thick stemmed Webster variations.

When the stems are dry enough to snap like sticks, this material can be put through a hammermill to add to the pig ration, and the following results are from the 1953 harvest.

	Protein per cent	Fibre per cent
Sample 1. Yorkshire	25·2	14·4
Sample 2. Yorkshire	21·51	19·7
Sample 3. Kent	22·15	11·4

This method is recommended for goat keepers who feed it in winter as a source of protein and minerals. The lower grade Hungarian dried comfrey imported by herbalists for extracting the allantoin with alcohol to make tinctures, is probably prepared in this way.

Tripods have been tried in Britain, but if comfrey waits about in the open in a wet season the proteins begin to break down. In Kenya and Rhodesia haymaking is easier, provided the crop is cut at the leafy stage and just left in the sun, perhaps turned by hand or machine once. This can be done in the U.S.A. but is difficult in rainy Britain.

Leaving the crop to wilt almost to hay in the field and then putting it through a shredder and a grass drier will reduce the fuel cost considerably, but it is the last 40 per cent of moisture that is hardest to take out.

Pelleting and Cubing

These methods of drying by pressure have all been used on a laboratory scale and many samples have been made. The need is for trials to get the machinery right, and then to undertake stock feeding tests before marketing the product. Growing the comfrey is no trouble at all.

6. Comfrey for pigs and poultry

Every writer since 1810 has stressed the real pleasure pigs have in eating comfrey; there is never any question of their getting accustomed to it by degrees, and one has only to offer a troughful to receive a very quick answer to the statement that 'no stock will eat it'. Pigs will eat a great many things greedily including soil and cinders if their mineral nutrition is neglected, and comfrey supplies minerals in digestible form as well as the high protein and low fibre that suits their dietary needs.

The late Kenneth Crawley fattened pigs on comfrey plus swill through the War years, and found when meal became available, that roughly half could be replaced with comfrey *ad lib.*, and later experience shows that fishmeal can be cut right out of the ration with a saving that increases as prices rise.

There are many ways of feeding comfrey to pigs and Vernon Stephenson developed one entirely of his own. He kept five acres under permanent pasture near his house for an exercise paddock, and rested these under Essex pigs, which are the best grazers. They were on 90-foot tether chains and accommodated in 'pigloos' moved across the paddock to alter the balance of herbage and destroy any parasite worms from horses that might appear. It is possible to run mares and foals and riding horses (but not stallions) with breeding sows in pig harness, to prevent the build-up of docks and nettles that occurs in Britain on any pasture permanently grazed by horses, and this system is recommended for riding stables.

The cut comfrey for each tethered pig was thrown down outside the pigloo in varied quantity, building up to a maximum of 30 lb. a day for a gilt just before sale, and to fit the appetite of a sow with a growing litter. As a general average he found he could save 25 per cent of the meal that would be fed to pigs on this grazing system.

The most profitable policy was to feed to pork weight because baconers required more carbohydrate meal, and over the years his stock had built up a reputation with local butchers for leaner pork and earned a premium for this quality.

The quantity of comfrey available varied with the number of mares at stud and the number of show jumpers under training, for these rather than the pigs had the comfrey. Though 'roof top hay' was made for the horses in winter, only the boar and breeding sows plus replacement gilts were kept then. The aim was to clear out the pigs when the comfrey went dormant.

A trial was undertaken at the Devon Farm Institute at Bicton, with a twentieth of an acre of comfrey planted in September 1958. The first trial involved only four pigs whose live weight averaged 99 lb. These were each fed 3 lb. of fattening meal a day with comfrey to appetite until time of slaughter at 145 lb. in 28 days— each pig eating 1 cwt. fattening meal and 2 cwt. comfrey. Further trials showed that 1 lb. fattening meal could be replaced with 5 lb. of fresh comfrey. As a basic rule, a pig should eat up to 10 per cent of its body weight in addition to fattening meal.

A test at the Fujisawa Farm of the Nihon Agricultural University in Japan showed that adult pigs do well on 8 to 9 kg. (17 to 19 lb.) of green leaf per day. This means replacing 30 per cent of the meal with cut comfrey. The University report states 'a noticeable result was the improved health of the pigs fed on comfrey' not only from the allantoin, which banished scouring, but better mineral balance. This was also observed at the Devon farm institute.

General Sir Philip Christison, whose yields are reported earlier bought in store pigs and grew them on to pork weight on comfrey to gain the usual 25 to 30 per cent saving on meal, and plenty of manure for his nitrogen-greedy blackcurrant orchard. In 1969 he made a 5 cwt. batch of vacuum silage, wilted for twenty-four hours and sealed it in 500-gauge polythene bags which were then subjected to 18 mercuries vacuum. An analysis by the West of Scotland Agricultural College showed the following.

	per cent
Moisture	86·5
Dry matter	13·5
Crude protein in dry matter	34·0
Crude fibre	19·2
Carbohydrate	6·0

This could be an answer to the winter pig feeding problem, but there are further processes under trial that may find the answer to so much protein and water and too little carbohydrate and fibre.

Perhaps the greatest profits have been made by feeding unlimited comfrey to the runts, nisgards, wrecklings, caddies, and all the other names for the small pig in the litter. The late Charles Rogers, a retired pigman of St. Austell, made a good living by buying up all these variously named rejects on Cornish markets, and rearing them for sale as stores after this comfrey treatment. His yield was only 20 tons an acre, but with runts, and buying up any pigs that were scouring so the price was down, to sell cured with comfrey, his plot was probably earning more for its size than any other in the 1955 race.

The most profitable branch of pig farming for comfrey is store raising, feeding it *ad lib*. to sows with too many piglets for their teats. The stronger piglets will start eating leafy comfrey very early which gives a chance to the weaklings which almost enjoy a system of two sittings for meals. Where a boar carries the genes for large litters there may well be as many as four teatless piglets and the less milk the unlucky ones receive the smaller and weaker they are and the more meals they miss.

Mrs. P. B. Greer used to time her farrowings for early April so the first cuts fitted the sow and the crop grew with the demands of the piglets. Mr. George Halling of Stevenage has about three and a half acres of comfrey which he has fed to horses and sheep, but its main value is fed to his breeding sows which vary up to a hundred according to the state of the pig market. In his opinion, 'If you average eight reared to a litter you barely hold your own, nine means you are making a living, with ten you are doing nicely and at twelve you are in the money'.

In his view the second most important aspect of comfrey on the modern piggery was as a disposal area for slurry, for he found that it was possible to continue irrigating with this right through the winter without harming the crop. Rotavation between the rows to keep the grass down was best in the autumn so the crop started the winter clean; and resting half of it each year for liming, at about two tons an acre, kept the land from becoming too acid. This adds the saving from not installing an aeration trench and not paying for treatment of the slurry which must now be kept out of rivers and drainage systems at the risk of heavy fines, to the reduction in the cost of protein feeds.

In 1953, when the first version of this book was binding, I went down to Stock (Essex) and saw the late Mr. George Webster, who drove me to Leigh-on-Sea to visit one of his best customers, whose name I cannot remember after more than twenty years. This elderly pig breeder had a boar named Tom and four sows built on the lines of hippos, which he claimed were regularly producing twenty-two piglets a litter, and twenty-six was their record. He fed cut comfrey plus swill and chat potatoes and the evidence was that the minerals in the comfrey balanced up the heavy demand on the sows' milk from such throngs of piglets.

I have never seen so many piglets in such a jumble of strawbales, corrugated iron, mud and comfrey plants and there certainly were twenty-three round Maggie, the largest of the sows. The piglets were sold as weaners or stores to smallholders and made very good prices with maximum level batches at every farrowing.

The comfrey fed to the piglets was always young leaves without any coarse stems full of fibre from allowing plants to run to flower. Adult pigs will eat any comfrey, but it pays to cut frequently and with care for piglets, just as it does with poultry.

Comfrey for Poultry

The digestion of the fowl is even less fibre-tolerant than that of the pig. It is simple and contains no bacteria able to digest cellulose, and the stomach secretes no enzyme which can deal with it. Therefore, though a pig can get some nourishment out of the 'digestible fibre' portion of his diet—a negligible quantity compared to the horse or to cattle whose digestions are adapted to fit the high-fibre grasses—with the fowl, fibre is an active disadvantage.

When the crude fibre of any ration reaches 10 per cent, there may be a reduction in the digestibility of the carbohydrates; at higher rates this is certain to produce a heavy fall in egg yields and delayed maturity, however rich the rest of the diet. The crude fibre should vary between 5 and 8 per cent of the total diet, and the nearer the lower limit the better, though this small proportion is of value in keeping the food mixture in a more open condition on its relatively short journey, and allowing the digestive juices to have the maximum effect. As Sussex-ground oats, as an example, are right up at the limit, 10·3 per cent, less fibrous foods must balance the diet at a lower level. Though in nature a flock of jungle fowl would eat considerable quantities of green food, and obtain plenty of 'animal' protein from insects and even small lizards, they are not endeavouring to return a profit measured to within three places of decimals in fractions of a penny per bird. Green fodder is today valued purely as a means of providing some exercise, some interest in meal-times (which prevents cannibalism and 'vice') and vitamin A. Its eclipse, except in the backyard where a swinging brussels sprout stem or a handful of chickweed is the feathered world's equivalent to the arrival of mail or Red Cross parcels, is due to the knowledge that it overloads the digestive system with bulk and fibre, to the exclusion of more nutritious foods.

Comfrey provides a low fibre high protein, high mineral feed, which can replace more costly concentrates, especially if it is kept cut so that there are no tough flower stems. The deep-litter system (known as 'built-up litter' in the U.S.A.), which is the only practical method of composting shavings, is ideal in tropical countries, where the cellulose breaks down more completely than in Britain, but leaves behind the lasting lignins which build up something in the way of humus.

Mr. L. G. Fairchild, a bacteriologist of Chingola, in what is now Zambia, developed a method of combining comfrey and deep litter to make it possible to grow eggs and table birds to European quality. Native breeds are specialized to scratch along without green food during the dry season, but those who have eaten the skinny fowls and tiny pale-yolked eggs of the tropics will realize that raising poultry keeping to European standards, with British or American breeds, could double food production.

Compost heaps as we know them can be unsatisfactory in hot climates because the breakdown is too complete, but deep litter provides a valuable means of building up fertility. Other materials than shavings and sawdust have been used, but not more than 10 per cent of sugar cane bagasse should be included because the residual sugar can become alcohol and cause complications in the breakdown of the litter. Very fine and dusty materials, such as refuse coconut fibre, can bind together and exclude the air, but barks are highly suitable as they are rich in minerals, though lower in cellulose, and worth putting through a shredder, if available in quantity. Up to 20 per cent of paper waste can be added to the litter and breaks down well, despite the presence of printer's ink which does not appear to bother the bacteria concerned.

The deep litter system depends on a number of bacteria that are specialized to break down straw with the readily available nitrogen in cattle urine which live in farmyards. The dab of white on chicken's droppings is the urine, and its ammonium carbonate is what makes battery manure too 'fierce' to use in the garden, except on comfrey. The bacteria grab this nitrogen to make up their bodies (plus the phosphorus in which poultry manure is also rich) as they increase to break down most of the cellulose and some of the hemicelluloses, producing just as much heat as if they had burnt it, and needing exactly as much oxygen, so ventilation is all important. The heat dries off the poultry manure so that in Rhodesia it is about 13 per cent moisture, and holds nearly as much potash as nitrogen, because of the potassium released from the wood. The table on page 107 shows how this compares with British deep litter samples, and it will be seen that the by-product of the Fairchild poultry system is a balanced general fertilizer dry enough to bag and sell.

In Britain or America a deep litter house is a solid wooden building insulated to hold the heat in, for the warmth from the bacterial 'bonfire' slowly breaking down the shavings helps winter laying. In Africa the problem is to get rid of the heat, and Mr. Fairchild sites his houses where the Trade Wind blows through the wire netting sides, and his asbestos roofing is whitewashed for lowest sunlight absorption. A black surface absorbs heat, and even a bitumen-painted corrugated iron shed can get hot inside, in even an English summer. It is attention to detail that makes a good poultry keeper of any colour in any country.

The following account is quoted from Mr. Fairchild's report to the Henry Doubleday Research Association:

'Experience has shown that orthodox deep litter methods in the tropics are not practical and most so called deep litter enthusiasts sooner or later switch to a modified form of strawyard or outside run. Many "deep litter" projects I have seen in Central Africa are essentially run on these lines.

'When I first started deep litter at Portmore I found the houses were too dark and too hot, the birds sweated and then got colds, and broodiness, even in leghorn crosses was rife.

'After a season of this during which I had a large outbreak of roup I constructed outside runs of a size equivalent to the house area but soon found the birds to be infested with lice. Later when the rains came the outside runs, in spite of tons of straw cover, became unusable and the birds were put back into the houses with a consequent drop in egg production.

'Definitely a new system had to be devised if deep litter was to be an economical proposition in this part of the world. Under our own local conditions arks and range shelters were not practical owing to the theft hazard and birds of prey, straw yards worked very well during the dry season, although lice were troublesome, but were impossible during the rainy season (50 inches of rain in five months): deep litter therefore was the only answer.

'Another very important feature was the saving in labour to be gained from a well organized deep litter set up. This was obviously the answer to local poultry keeping problems and we set out to devise a practical economic and, as far as possible, foolproof system which would overcome such hazards as theft, climatic variations, native unreliability and so on.

'Three or four temporary houses were built with pole and dagga (mud) having a rough thatch roof, and results over a season were noted. The best results were obtained from a house for 200 birds measuring 60' × 12' having its long axis sited east to west. This house consisted of a 2' wall with 6″ pillars at ten foot intervals to support the roof. The open spaces between the wall and roof were then covered with wire netting. The production figures for this house were 67 per cent for the season which is above average for the tropics.

'Following this experiment, seven permanent houses were constructed of bricks made and burnt on the farm and these were roofed with iron or asbestos. The spaces between the pillars were covered, on the inside aspect, with heavy gauge 2″ wire netting. Roof trusses were made from $4\frac{1}{2}″ × 1″$ oregon with a 3' pitch and $4″ × 3″$ timbers were used for cross members.

'The houses were spaced 15 feet apart as this was calculated to let in the maximum amount of light with the minimum amount of rain, and at the same time allow an adequate space in which to grow greenfood for the laying birds.

'The houses were stocked and during the first season gave very good results with no illness. The areas between the houses became covered with a very fine dust from the litter during the dry season and during the first rainy season these plots planted to lucerne which came away in lush growth without fertilizer or innoculant.

'The lucerne, however, died off in the dry season and we found ourselves, like everybody else in these parts short of greenfood.

'About this time the possibilities of Russian Comfrey came to my notice and one plot was planted to this herb which grew well and gave green food all through the dry season. Yields of Comfrey were not measured but an experimental irrigated bed yielded 66 tons of fresh green food to the acre in its first year and in its second year scaled 85 tons to the acre.

'All the plots between the houses are now planted to Russian Comfrey at 60 plants a piece which yield an average of $2\frac{1}{2}$ lbs. green food per plant per month unwatered.

1. Henry Doubleday (1813–1902), Quaker smallholder and introducer of the first F_1 hybrid comfrey into England. From a daguerrotype taken at the 1851 Exhibition.

2. Close-up of a comfrey flower. Comfrey rarely sets seed. In the process of hybridization the small triangles that fit over the stamens have inherited two strong 'hinges' to open up and let the bees in.

3. Section of a comfrey flower. This shows the 'false bottom' that makes bees bite in through the side and only pollenate if they try the 'front door' when they have pollen on their heads.

4. Vernon Stephenson in one of the comfrey plots at Hunsley House Stud, near Hull, Yorkshire, where comfrey was fed to racehorses for nearly forty years.

5. Feeding stallion. Phideas, one of the many stallions kept fit and productive on the diet of wheat cavings (for starch equivalent) and comfrey that saves money for riding stables.

6. Feeding calves. Mrs. P. B. Greer bought calves that were 'scouring' in Colchester market and cured them on chopped comfrey in their milk bucket feeding for rearing on her pastures.

7. Piglets. The strongest piglets in litters of up to 22 scamper off to eat comfrey fed generously to the sow, and give the weaker ones a chance at the teats, which puts up the average reared to 12–14.

8. Part of a comfrey field at Nakuru, Kenya, owned by Mr. J. McInnes, then secretary of the Kenya Milk Recording scheme, which holds the world's record yield of 124 tons 15 cwt. per acre in 1955. The equal day length near the equator gives year round production and twelve monthly cuts totalled over 15 tons an acre dry matter.

9. Giraffes at Whipsnade Zoo. Giraffes also relish comfrey especially when their bones are building and they need calcium and phosphate in readily available form, even more than racehorse foals.

10. Bocking No. 14 comfrey on the H.D.R.A. Trial Ground, with a 40 ton an acre yield. The thin stems, high potash and high allantoin of this variety, which is rust resistant, make it perhaps the best British garden variety.

11. Part of a 3½ acre comfrey field at Stevenage, Herts., owned by George Halling who used it to feed a 100 sow breeding unit. Its value to him lies in replacing an expensive aeration trench with a cheap protein supply.

12. Elmer Jeskey of Aurora, Oregon, has six acres of comfrey which he feeds as a supplement to pasture for bullocks, gaining an extra 100 lb. a beast at eight months old. He is offering them baled hay made with comfrey.

13. He cuts the crop with a silorator towed behind an old Case tractor kept permanently attached to the machine and trailer.

14. The trailer is large enough to take one day's ration at maximum stocking and appetite, and one trip up and down his long field is enough to fill it.

15. Phil Phillips looking at Elmer Jeskey's comfrey weeder. The centre tines are removed from a standard 36 inch Howard rota-vator, to weed a 14 inch wide strip each side of the row.

16. The gap fits over the plants and the tines each side throw the cultivated soil flat to avoid ridges that interfere with silorator harvesting. An old Ferguson tractor is permanently attached to this machine to keep the crop clean.

17. Every three years a potato lifter is run through the crop to take up roots for propagation. Elmer Jeskey with a sack of root cuttings which sell at three hundred dollars for enough to plant an acre.

'When established this plant is drought resistant and requires no watering through the dry season (although irrigation would increase its yields), and with its constant fertilizing from the dust of hens working the litter, it comes away with great gusto at the first shower of rain.

'The litter used is sawdust and shavings which is thought to react with the droppings to produce a fertilizer of high potash content which Russian Comfrey really needs. Whether this is so in actual fact has yet to be proved but the results certainly support the theory.

'The preliminary stages of this system give great promise of a trouble free labour saving system of poultry keeping in the tropics and compared with other systems does not require excessive capital outlay.

'Mash has been fed *ad lib.*, in four 6' double sided hoppers per house. These are topped up weekly and water is laid on by a flat valve controlling a 6' drinker. This drinker is mounted on a platform in front of the broody cages at the end of each house so that the free and captive birds can all drink at once. 40 gallon drums are mounted outside each house to feed the drinkers, and these drums are filled daily by hosepipe. Nest tunnels are made with old corrugated iron sheets leaning against the side walls.

'One native worker is required for each set of seven houses and his task includes cleaning one house thoroughly daily, i.e. scraping perches, turning litter, brushing the wire, topping up hoppers and cleaning the drinker—this usually occupies him for 2–3 hours. Other duties consist of collecting eggs at 10 a.m., 12 noon, 2 p.m. and 4 p.m. cutting, chaffing and feeding Comfrey at noon and feeding grain at 4 p.m. During this final round at 5.30 p.m. he collects broodies and puts them into confinement.

'The birds, mainly light Sussex and New Hampshires, are kept for two seasons being force moulted after the first year.

'No illness has been noted since the installation of this system and vices are non existent. No lice and no worms have been found in any of these birds slaughtered for table and the deep orange yolks of the eggs compare favourably with the pale yolks common to Central Africa.

5

'The advantages of this self contained system are numerous.

1. Economy of labour and ease of checking on the unreliable labour usually available in this country.

2. Equable temperature of the houses described whether under iron or asbestos.

3. The birds grow their own green food. The dust from the houses contains what the Russian Comfrey likes and the Comfrey certainly contains the vital ingredients of a hen's diet in palatable form.

4. The orientation of the houses allows the morning sun and afternoon sun to flood the ends of the houses with its rays while the birds are shaded from the scorching mid-day sun.

5. Ample ventilation day and night.

'Flaws in the system as yet discovered are few and are apt to be of local significance only. One such instance which occurred at Portmore was that we found predatory animals would molest and even kill birds roosting near the wire at night. That was the reason for erecting the wire netting on the *inner* side of the pillars to stop birds from perching on the walls, and of course, all perches are now sited along the centre of each house. Minor problems might be encountered according to locality but the modern farmer is seldom without ideas or the capacity to carry them out.

'One final word I would like to say about Russian Comfrey which is well liked by the birds, is its eminent suitability as a poultry diet—its protein fibre ratio is in the region of $1\frac{1}{2}:1$ in contrast to young lucernes which is rather $1:1\frac{1}{2}$ and, this, added to the fact that it grows well without water for many months in scorching heat make it a green crop worthy of consideration in any deep litter system similar to the one described above and especially for the farmer in the tropics.'

The Chingola poultry system was tried in Japan by a Mr. Suzuki of Yokosuka to see if it would pay in his country where the squeeze between rising food costs and egg and table bird prices is just as tight as in other countries.

He fed equal parts of the chopped foliage and his normal meal ration to 2,000 mature birds and 1,000 pullets from April 1963 to

November 1963 when the crop goes dormant for the winter in Japan, just as it does in England. His other 3,000 birds were given no comfrey in this trial supervised by Mr. Hosaka, veterinarian to the Kokosuka Agricultural Co-operative.

The first results were a saving of 790,000 yen (about £790 at 1964 exchange rates) on feed costs and a rise in egg production to 70 to 75 per cent (100 per cent = one egg a day for every bird) which fell when the comfrey stopped in November, to 60 to 65 per cent, the same as the ordinary meal fed birds. There was also improved egg quality shown in yolk colour, and better growth of the younger birds, with pullets maturing to egg production 15 to 20 days sooner than when no comfrey was fed.

Comfrey was also fed to table birds and was found to produce rather yellower flesh than normal because of the extra vitamin A compared with broilers on a ration without greenfood. In Britain the broiler industry considers that the public will buy only white fleshed chickens, though we prefer brown eggs because of their 'country farmyard appearance'. It is possible that if table birds were fed comfrey as in Japan the public might well prefer them to tasteless broilers. The yellower flesh would be a guarantee that the birds had been given green food.

A British experiment with comfrey feeding on the deep litter system was carried out by an H.D.R.A. member, Mr. F. Roscoe of Henby Dale near Huddersfield. On 21 May 1964 he bought twelve R.R. × L.S. pullets at five weeks old, and kept them in a wired off portion of his standard deep litter house. After trying out several ways of feeding comfrey he got them taking a good daily ration at sixteen weeks old and at 20 weeks they commenced to lay. After four weeks he lost one bird. The egg total was then 109 eggs, an average of nine a bird. He kept on the experiment with the remaining eleven.

The best method of feeding comfrey was hanging up a bunch on a string so the birds could jump for it, wasting none by treading it into the litter. It was supplied *ad lib.* from the first cut in March till late November, with the usual mash, an evening feed of pellets and a handful of grain and scraps during the day for variety.

In the words of Mr. Roscoe: 'They were always eager to snatch the comfrey from my arms as I entered the house and I learnt to bring in a mug of grain to throw to the far end of the house to get them away from my feet.'

They continued to lay for 61 weeks before moulting in September 1965 with 106 eggs in the last four weeks.

Mr. Roscoe kept accounts and his results are summarized as follows:

	£	p
Cost of pullets	4	80
Cost of mash, pellets and grain	20	36½
	25	16½
Total eggs sold 205·9 dozen	39	37½
Eggs for home use 24·9 dozen		
Total eggs 230·6 dozen	14	21 profit

At a conservative estimate Mr. Roscoe considers that he saved £4 on food by using comfrey, and in addition to his 24·9 dozen eggs for home eating he had about a ton of deep litter poultry manure (his litter was a mixture of sawdust, shavings, bracken, dead leaves and peat) for his garden. He will use it to activate about two-thirds more garden rubbish.

He has a bed of 100 comfrey plants spaced two feet apart each way and cut roughly at six week intervals, but these supply enough to use wilted in his potato trenches and as compost material as well as for poultry greenfood.

Mr. Roscoe's house is 18 ft × 11 ft., 6 ft. to ridge, with side windows, baffles and the top and wire netting ventilators below. The house, which never holds more than 50 birds, has a 'pophole' so the birds can take exercise outside, but Mr. Roscoe kept this closed while he was feeding comfrey. He considered that as chickens have a limited appetite, if they filled up with less nutritious grazing outside they would have no room for enough comfrey to cut the costs. In his opinion the saving on comfrey feeding with deep litter should make all the difference between profit and loss on a large scale, for £3 to £4 a dozen birds off feed costs adds up to hundreds of pounds a week on the scale of modern poultry farms.

He decided to run his birds on for a second season and reported:

'After my experiments from May 1964 I resolved to take the eleven pullets now fully grown, on to another year's laying with the best of my even older hens, with a view of finding what comfrey had to offer to offset the anticipated smaller amount of eggs and also to find any difference at the end of laying as a table bird. When comfrey-cutting was over in November one found the egg production gradually lowering and one had difficulty in finding sufficient green vegetable for them. For nothing now takes the place of *Comfrey*. However, when spring comes round and with it comfrey one does not need to ask for an invitation to enter the house, nor does the mug of corn thrown well in, act any more. They are older and wiser birds. They relish meeting again their long lost friend with great gusto. Gradually the egg output rises with a noticeable deeper yolk once more. As the weeks go by into summer one finds a mid morning feed followed by a later afternoon one of comfrey can be given. All the time the usual mash is in the hopper to take as required, together with an occasional handful of corn and scraps. About one third of their capacity now consists of comfrey. Egg output is retained all the time and while being somewhat less than the pullet year, size of egg is on the whole larger. Come autumn and time for despatch arrives. After preparing for the table, the birds were sold to various customers and a consensus of opinion on quality etc., colour when prepared for the table, would seem to indicate complete satisfaction.

'On the question of flesh colour, after two years feeding on comfrey the birds certainly are less white, more inclined to cream, but culinarily speaking no different. The full picture which now emerges is, that a moderate number of birds supplementary fed on comfrey certainly pay well over two years. For me at least, comfrey and poultry or vice-versa are symbiotic. Comfrey to feed Poultry. Poultry Manure to feed Comfrey.'

The extra vitamin A from comfrey feeding should in theory

produce the yellow flesh which Japanese customers prefer, but their breeds are bred for darker flesh, unlike our market which is supposed to demand broiler whiteness, achieved by feeding buckwheat and various additives.

Mr. Roscoe, Mr. Suzuki and Mr. Fairchild were all growing Bocking Mixture plants, and these large leafed, solid stemmed comfreys are by far the best for poultry. The Stephenson strain is mainly Bocking 14, and this made possible his weeding system.

The Stephenson System

The main comfrey plot at Hunsley House was for many years weeded by running a flock of about a hundred layers over its half acre area. These birds were housed in an ordinary wheeled free-range house with dropping boards, which was moved from one end of the plot to the other because poultry will range over a very small area near the house which they will tread and peck bare, unless their house position is changed.

Bocking No. 14 is unpopular with chickens unless it is wilted and chaffed, so provided they are not starved of green food, the birds will eat the weeds between the rows rather than the plants, which merely suffer occasional pecking. The poultry droppings are spread by the birds, and the dropping boards emptied between the rows, with additional manure from the battery and deep-litter houses. The horse manure from the stud sold for such a good price to mushroom growers that it was never used on the comfrey.

An experiment at the Harper Adams College with increased green food produced the following results: $2\frac{1}{2}$ ounces per bird per day were fed to eight-week-old pullets and layers to provide 10 per cent of the dry matter of the mash. The green food was grass mowings, 80 per cent moisture, and the result was delayed maturity for the young birds, and for the hens a 50 per cent drop in egg yields.

The same feeding system was tried by Mr. E. V. Stephenson with his laying battery, feeding $2\frac{1}{2}$ to 3 ounces a head of wilted comfrey per day, with no fall in egg yield, and a saving in concentrates amounting to an ounce a day per bird. He states that his birds were in perfect health and if the daily comfrey ration was missed, they became unsettled and unhappy. The great advantage was the ease of cutting and supplying the same green fodder from April to November, with none of the difficulties of sowing and raising successive green fodder crops. The gap in winter was filled with stored carrots and swedes.

This was, of course, a single experiment, carried out in four successive seasons with the same result, and whatever the in-accuracies of weighing, it does show that one experienced poultry keeper has fed considerably in excess of the normal green food allowance and made a considerable saving in meal. As the battery was used during the war for this experiment, the concentrates were not only expensive but rationed.

The comfrey was wilted down to approximately 75 per cent moisture, before being put through a chaff-cutter and incorporated with the mash. At this stage its carotene would be nearly the same as that of fresh grass in spring (see the previous chapter), and ample vitamin A would mean a good colour in the egg yolks for the whole period. The fibre would be 3 per cent, which would be approximately the same as that of the lawn mowings, and there would be rather more digestible protein.

The normal green food ration, to provide vitamin A and vitamin B complex, is roughly one ounce a day, fed as wilted-brassica green matter (such as kales), but there is evidence from the past, of an enthusiastic but unfortunately non-statistical nature, that chickens will eat very much more than this when wilted comfrey is supplied. This may be due to the taste, to the allantoin, or to the fact that its fibres are few and do not harden round the surface as the crop wilts. Because it is the cheapest of all sources of vitamin A in terms of labour, it deserves extensive experiment by poultry stations, and by private poultry farmers, first on the ounce-a-day level, and then increasing to cash its food value in the maximum saving of purchased meal without a fall in egg production.

For deep litter poultry, Mr. Stephenson supplied a regular three ounces a day, very roughly, which was always cleared up, and considered that he saved some meal, sufficient to make cutting and feeding on this scale pay well.

Though comfrey seems of considerable value to growing

poultry, before eight weeks old it should be fed chaffed. The fibres are few but stringy, and there is a risk of crop trouble with young chicks. This is avoided by making sure that it is in short lengths. Exactly the same trouble occurs with grass, but as the season goes on and grass and other fodder crops run to cellulose and stem, the risk increases; with well-cut comfrey, which is a series of 'springs' so far as the foliage is concerned, the risk stays low.

Hand chaff cutters are rare today, but anyone rearing poultry on comfrey would find a Sheen Compost Shredder with a 2½ h.p. engine extremely useful to chop up the most stemmy material into short lengths. There are many machines of this type in America, and one of the least powerful will serve.

Weeding by poultry is essentially a small scale idea that appeals to the forgotten men of the feathered world—the backyard poultry keepers.

The smallest number of plants to start with is thirty, giving a cut of one a day, though as they increase in size there is nothing to prevent cutting half or less. With seven-pound plants in the second or third year, and three ounces per bird about the maximum they will eat in a day, there is soon a balance at the end of the month for compost, which can run on for another fortnight as there is no need to aim at high protein for the heap. Poultry will clean more comfrey than they can possibly eat, about 24 square yards per bird, and the minimum backyard runs space recommended by the Harper Adams College is 25 square feet, a space 5 feet long and 5 feet wide. It is therefore possible to wire in the comfrey corner, providing green-stuff only when the plants are small, and compost as well as they increase in size.

The space needed for thirty plants only, three feet apart in six rows of five plants each with eighteen inches of space at the ends and sides, is fifteen feet by twenty-one feet. This is enough for twelve birds, and as soon as each cut averages three pounds per plant easily (and the Rev. E. Highton got six pounds his first year in good garden soil in 1875), their entire green food ration is supplied from this minimum run area. It is better, if space allows, to make two runs, either with fifteen plants in each and the balance bare land, or further plants for compost, so that they can be used alternately. As spring planting has a considerable spread-over, the first run can be planted in March with the birds in the second, so that the comfrey will be up to cutting size and beyond injury risk from being pecked at when very young by late April. Then the birds are turned into the planted run, and a further batch is bought to stock the empty one. Autumn planting is not recommended, for though the poultry do not harm dormant established comfrey in winter, they will scratch up and eat new-planted crowns before these get a root hold.

Mrs. Quin-Smith of the Isle of Wight combines poultry and goat keeping on comfrey, using the Stephenson weeding system:

'In April 1965 two plots of Mr. E. V. Stephenson's comfrey were planted three feet apart each way. Plot A with 84 plants and Plot H with 42. In August 1965 Plot A was included in the chicken run. The chickens were not very interested in comfrey unless it was cut and left on the ground. They scratched their corn which was thrown between the plants and this kept the weeds down. Plot H was weeded between by Merrytiller and the plants were cut for the goats who liked it very much as an extra—it was fed in their hay rack.

'In October 1965 weeds from the potatoes next to Plot A, including couch roots, thistle and fleabane were thrown into the chickens in Plot A. Then bracken and straw were put down to be scratched and broken up by the fowls. Their corn was thrown into this until February 1966 when the chickens were moved and Plot A left to grow, with the first cuts in April and then an increasing yield through the summer.

'Plot H was composted in winter and in April 1966 was included in a large run with a substantial fence of chainlink round it for goats and chickens, ½ an acre of which ¼ acre is old pasture and a herbal mixture.

'Through the summer of 1966 both plots grew well and Plot A was fed to the goats, roughly two plants a day for 3 goats, and if it started growing away it was cut, wilted and composted. Plot H was grazed by the goats and the chickens kept it weedfree. If after rain plants became dirty on either plot and the goats would not eat them because of the mud splashed on the leaves, or if Plot H started to flower, I would cut the plants concerned to ground level and leave it on the ground, and the chickens would clear it. They seemed to like the coarse flowering stems but would not always eat the large leaves from Plot A which were mud splashed.'

It should be noted that those who use the system of weeding with poultry must plant a strain that is basically Bocking No. 14, which has other garden advantages described in Chapter 8. Weeding a Bocking Mixture or Bocking No. 4 with chickens can mean plants pecked to tatters.

There is, however, real evidence of the difference between battery and free range eggs, and the following quotation from Newsletter No. 9 of the 'Farm and Food Society' is of interest to those who are concerned with food value as well as freedom:

'The analysis of eggs is a very costly business and not easily productive of decisive proof, the experimenter being often more interested in proving a theory of his own than in establishing the truth. Members of the Co-ordinating Committee on Factory Farming, after a visit to Dr. Sainsbury's poultry units at the School of Veterinary Medicine at Cambridge brought back six eggs from battery hens and six from hens of the same hybrid at the same age and fed the same food in the open-fronted strawyards. The following table shows the analysis made by a firm of bio-chemical consultants of these eggs:

	S(*trawyard*)	B(*attery*)
Protein (Nx 6·38)	13·02 per cent	13·14 per cent
Fat	10·85 per cent	10·02 per cent
Riboflavin	0·31 mg/100g	0·26 mg/100g
Nicotinic Acid (Niacin)	0·961 mg/100g	0·045 mg/100g
Pantothenic Acid	1·90 mg/100g	2·17 mg/100g
Vitamin B12	0·73 mcg/100g	0·42 mcg/100g
Moisture	73·5 per cent	72·0 per cent
Vitamin A	1,500 I.U./100g	1,500 I.U./100g

'(Note by analyst: The most dramatic difference is in the figures for vitamin B12 (anti-pernicious anaemia factor) in the two samples. This I regard as really serious, especially for vegetarians, who are entirely dependent for their supply of this vitamin on eggs and milk. I also think the riboflavin and niacin content of Sample B are significantly lower than S.)'

The essential appears to be contact with the soil and the availability of worms, for the comparison is between battery and *strawyard*, not free range, and most backyard poultry keepers can provide at least a run which can be dug over at intervals, with room to grow comfrey for the summer, and kale or cabbage for the winter green food supply. This must be rotated to avoid clubroot, and it cannot be used as a meal replacement because of its higher fibre.

Comfrey for Geese

Geese are grazing birds and will graze comfrey, but leave the midribs. They should therefore be confined with hurdles on an area they will clear in two days and then be moved to another run, and left leaves and stems being cut over to grow again. No detailed experimental results are available but Member Paul N. Griesenaur of the U.S. found that geese could be reared on an almost all comfrey diet.

'On April 28th 1958, I received two dozen Emden goslings two days old. All were fed nothing but "mushed" Comfrey for four weeks. At this end, one dozen was put out on range where they had free access to Comfrey plants in the field and a large area of Ladino Clover. The others remained in a small pen or enclosure having good shade and plenty of water in a trough. The Comfrey which they consumed was all reduced to a mush until June 24th. On June 17th I married again—a girl whom I had known about 40 years, I being a widower for 18 years—and, lest I forget, 72 years young—we took quite a lengthy trip as a part of a honeymoon. Upon our return on July 24th, I found that the "mushing machine" had become broken a few days after we had left on the trip. The geese were fed Comfrey leaves alone—all that they could consume, but without weighing. Up to June 24th the weighing record showed a total of 1908 pounds for 12 geese—for the 53 days, or an average of 3 pounds per day. The "mushing machine" apparently was not working properly—was not properly beating up the ribs which were not consumed by the geese as too woody, therefore it is hard to say just what was the actual consumption of the plant consumed.

'After my return no further weighing was done as I considered it useless. At the beginning of the tenth week, half a pound of yellow corn meal—per goose, was given in a trough in the form of a "mush", a total of 7 pounds per goose. Corn meal was bought at $3·25 per 100 pounds. The geese thus fed averaged 10 lbs. 2 oz. against 12 lbs. 3 oz. for like amount last year, only that those of last year were fed Comfrey mush during the entire twelve weeks. The geese of this year dressed an average of 7 lbs. and last year's crop averaged 8 lbs. 1 oz. The ones out on pasture were dressed December 8th and averaged but $7\frac{1}{2}$ pounds at 7 months and one week. The flesh of these left to roam was darker somewhat "stringy". The pen-fed were of a much superior quality, yet not as well commended as those of last year. The penned ones of this year had a somewhat struggle with the ribbed leaves. A Greek who runs one, if not the finest eating house here in the city, a man who is a connoisseur in fowl, and who bought four of the geese, stated that he had never tasted the like before, that the flesh could be cut with the fork alone. I, too, found this to be true.'

7. Comfrey for grazing animals

Horses have an entirely different temperament to cattle and sheep, even though all three are grazing animals, and the difference can be expressed in the fact that, though sheep dogs are well known, and there are cattle dogs like the Welsh corgi, no one has ever heard of a 'horse dog'.

When danger threatens, cattle bunch together and so do sheep, and a team of dogs and men can then drive them. The instinct of the stallion is to attack the danger, in company with his equals, giving the mares and foals time to get away. Then, when the enemy is defeated, the stallions race to overtake the herd, and today they will race round the paddock for the pleasure of the speed that is part of their lives right back to Eohippus and the horses which crossed the Bering Straits to the limitless plains of Siberia and Russia. A stallion will kill a dog that tries to 'herd him' and can kill a man, standing tall and terrible with death in his front hooves.

Horses graze for speed and they need minerals to build their bones. Mares in foal need calcium and phosphorus to build up the bones of wobbly-legged foals which can so soon follow the herd. All through the crucial years up to the date of the Derby, these minerals must be available to the young animals as they are needed to thicken and strengthen and make ever more dense the bones which take the shock of the thundering hooves as the favourite pulls ahead of the field into the straight.

You can put out mineral licks for cattle—artificial blocks of mineral salts which are slowly soluble—but not for horses. You can feed pigs on a scientifically balanced ration, but today they are fed quantities of copper salts to prevent pig anaemia. Of these they absorb only between 2 and 6 per cent and the balance passes through them to add up to copper toxicity in the pasture. Horses cannot be fed ground chalk in their racing mash, for they are no more able to absorb it than we are the chalk added to our paper-white bread to replace the calcium molecules chosen by the roots and stored in the germ and the bran of the wheat. Yet you cannot feed horses on wholemeal bread for they would get too much carbohydrate.

When you see horses swishing their tails under the trees in the paddock, notice how level the branches have been bitten off. A mare will rob her own bones for minerals to feed the foal inside her (so will every female animal), but she will stand staggering tall as a stallion to strip the bark off the twigs and thin branches which hold the most minerals.

I once led a mare called Lyon's Lass for a mile and a half along a country lane and let her graze as she would. She took yarrow, chicory and all the deep rooting herbs rather than the lushest grasses which were at their best in the full green tide of summer. Just like the cows at Southery leaving the pedigree Aberystwyth grasses for cut comfrey, she enjoyed her comfrey ration every day, for she knew what she wanted when she had a chance to get it.

At Hunsley House Stud, Stephenson Strain comfrey was fed *ad lib.* to working stallions, but when the ration had to be cut because of the needs of the mares, the regular allowance for all adult stock was 14 lb. a day from April to when the crop goes dormant in November, being replaced in winter with bought carrots for vitamin A. Only a small quantity of 'roof-top hay' can be made because of the needs of both pigs and horses, which are lowest in winter.

The gain from this is in avoiding digestive disturbances, urinary complaints and above all scouring in foals. Vernon Stephenson, who counted eleven Grand Nationals in his long life spent with horses, considered that banishing these troubles made it worth keeping a comfrey plot on every area of his extensive stud, so some could be cut and fed on the pasture with minimum labour. His object was not cash saving, though this was considerable, but to give good horses the best. He had the responsibility of at least fifty expensive mares a season, and found that 90 per cent of them took to wilted comfrey at once, and the remainder took to it with coaxing. They all went back to their owners in the pink of condition with their foals, but without any addition to their speed, except from general fitness.

A stable lad or groom may well tip one of his employer's horses as a winner, and be right, but he will not betray the secrets of the racing mash used in his stable. A trainer's concentrated feed before a race is an esoteric secret, which may even include stout, some of which may be enjoyed by his beasts, and there are trainers who add wilted and chaffed comfrey. However, I once had 'five bob' each way on the only comfrey-fed horse in the Derby, and though even the B.B.C. commentator remarked how fit and shiny-coated my choice looked, he finished far down the field, and I lost my five bob, which was worth far more than the twenty-five pence it has become. The usual allowance for horses in training, including show jumpers, is 6 lb. a day, which is fed because it lowers the risk of having to 'scratch'. Horses do not graze clover to any extent, though they will eat lucerne, and bunches of this are (or were) sold in Newmarket, to provide the essential fresh green food, which comfrey also provides.

Through the years the proportion of comfrey in the diet of the horses at Hunsley House has risen. The first stallion owned by Vernon Stephenson was Anatom, whom he was riding in the Grand National when both fell and broke their shoulders. The rider has the option of buying the injured horse for a nominal sum rather than letting it be shot, and Anatom went home with his rider, where both recovered. Anatom lived to the very great age, for a horse, of 22 years, and even towards the end of his life was siring show jumpers on mares of good hunter stock.

Like many stallions (and men) Anatom got rather bad tempered late in life, especially when his shoulder troubled him in wet weather, and his grooms learned that when the old gentleman was in the mood that means *The Times* thrown across the room, increasing the comfrey allowance was a remedy. When horses are fed concentrates they become extra frisky, hence the phrases 'full of beans' and 'feeling his oats', while extra green food has a certain tranquillizing effect, which is why the racing allowance is always lower than the normal ration. Or of course, the allantoin could have had an effect on the rheumatism in that long-broken shoulder.

The grooms found that Anatom would eat up to 40 lb. a day fresh weight, plus of course hay and oats, with quite a benefit to his temper. In 1953 Vernon Stephenson repeated the experiment of the Rev. E. Highton of Bude in 1875 (see Chapter 1), with Tom Atom, a four-year-old gelding sired by Anatom, feeding 40 lb. a day of comfrey and reducing the oats from 8 lb. a day to 4 lb. Tom Atom was working as a trainer's hack, for at the time Vernon Stephenson was training show jumpers, and hunting two days a week with the Holderness. The saving on hay then amounted to 17s. 6d. a week at 1953 prices.

Very many racing stables and riding schools buy in hay all the summer, partly from shortage of grazing space and mainly to feed a more concentrated diet. As hay matures in the stack till it looks like plug tobacco, some of the carbohydrates break down and the minerals become a larger part of its bulk. The changes which take place can be compared to those in ageing port, whisky or brandy, and can be recognized at once by connoisseurs. When old hay comes up for sale, racing stables will bid against each other and pay what farmers consider silly prices. Today there is less of this hay about, but the main saving Vernon Stephenson made on his comfrey was in not having to buy quite so much top quality hay, which had very much nearer the protein and mineral balance of the cheaper fodder. He continued to buy good hay, but he could afford to walk away from the sale with his money in his pocket if the price went above what he felt it was worth.

He then tried Tom Atom on a diet of comfrey and wheat cavings, which was in theory adequate, the comfrey providing the minerals and concentrated protein, and the cavings the digestible fibre to keep up the starch equivalent, without putting on weight. This worked perfectly with no hay at all, and Tom Atom carried out his duties through a second summer and continued through cubbing into Vernon Stephenson's essential two days a week hunting, ending the season so fit that he sold for a good price as a show jumper, a job in which we can hope he did not miss his comfrey.

Variations on these two basic diets, comfrey plus reduced oats and comfrey and cavings, could save a great deal of money today for riding schools, and livery stables, even though hay would still have to be bought or made to keep the beasts through the winter. The saving on every beast, with twenty years inflation which puts up the price of everything from saddle soap to hoof polish, would be nearer £13 a week, if of course the standard of comparison is the normal feeding on a first class stud. It is certain that a good, well kept comfrey plot would be an asset for anyone concerned with horses.

Comfrey for Cattle

An Indian H.D.R.A. member in the 1960s tried a variation of Tom Atom's diet on a pair of water buffaloes, feeding rice straw and comfrey, which he considered improved their 'drawbar pull', but he sold up the farm and moved to a city, so the experiment did not continue. We do not feed cattle for speed or energy, but for milk yield or live weight increase, and these demand not only minerals, for the 'solids not fat' fraction in the gallonage, but starch equivalent.

The late Kenneth Crawley estimated that 56 lb. a head of wilted comfrey would provide for maintenance and the first two gallons with his Ayrshires, but the problem of comfrey for cattle in Britain is that its bulk production comes when there is plenty of good grass. Cattle are designed as grass, legume and herb feeders, and comfrey provides the qualities of the last, plus protein, when this is already available. The cows at Southery would not have relished their comfrey so much had they been on a good organic farmer's herbal ley, instead of on pedigree grasses only.

Overseas the picture alters, even in a temperate climate like Japan's, where yields of 50 to 60 tons an acre are at British level, because grass is not the cheapest feed under their conditions. In mountainous Japan with a shortage of level acres, comfrey pays the milk producer. The following trial by the Meiji Milk Producing Co. was carried out in latitude 36°N, 75 miles W.N.W. of Tokyo in a valley 2,000 feet above sea level with high mountain ranges on both sides. In this country of steep slopes and small fields, comfrey paid well for dairy cows, and the following report from the

Japanese Comfrey Growers Association is unique as the first detailed record of its kind on dairy cattle.

Three cows, 'A' weighing 11 cwt., 'B' 10 cwt. 20 lb. and 'C' 9 cwt. 84 lb. were used in the trial, and in the weeks before and after the test week each cow got 4 lb. of concentrates and 44 lb. of ladine clover per day. In the test week 44 lb. of comfrey was substituted for the clover. They were also fed orchard grass and green oats at the following rates: Cow A, 97 lb. a day. Cow B, 105 lb. a day, Cow C, 82 lb. a day. The milk yields in the tables opposite are in pounds, and dividing by 10 to reduce to gallons is not quite accurate, as the density of the milk varies with breed, density and climate.

In addition to the main trial, palatability was tested separately: 44 lb. of comfrey per day was supplied to each of 6 cows, including A, B and C, for 7 days, and its palatability was observed. Each cow, A, B and C, took 11 lb. of comfrey in 20 minutes without hesitation. One of the six cows sniffed at first as it was new to them. As they got accustomed to it, they seemed to like comfrey as well as any other fodder.

Comfrey was supplied to a calf suffering from scours and as a result its droppings became firm. A continuous supply of comfrey to one cow also cured loose droppings. From these cases it can be concluded that comfrey contains an ingredient which has a corrective medical effect for the stomach and bowels.

This scour cure effect was used for many years by the late Mrs. P. B. Greer, who used to buy calves in Colchester market which were scouring and therefore cheap, sometimes very cheap, and bring them home to feed on goat's milk and comfrey. Leaves and stems put through a chaff cutter were fed in the bucket to start with, and, as with wreckling pigs, this produces a relatively large income from a small comfrey bed for anyone who knows stock. Old stock-men and pig-men are not concerned with protein, but, like Master Gerard, with allantoin, and this is at its highest in the stems up till flowering time, and after this the proportion falls, just as it does with oil of peppermint and the essential principles in many herbs.

In Britain today comfrey pays for calf rearing, fed in a hay net

CONVERSION OF MILK RECORD TABLE

Index numbers and percentage humidities are the same in both units. Yields are by weight only.

Period	Date		A lb.	B lb.	C lb.	Average lb.	Temperature Max. °F	Min. °F
Before feeding Comfrey	July	8	45·9	45·4	35·2	42·2	66·0	57·4
		9	46·6	44·2	35·4	42·1	71·0	56·5
		10	47·2	43·2	34·4	41·6	71·0	62·5
		11	44·0	44·0	33·2	40·4	72·0	64·0
		12	44·9	43·0	33·0	40·3	83·0	59·0
		13	47·8	43·2	34·1	41·7	79·5	62·0
		14	43·3	45·4	35·4	41·4	78·6	58·0
	Average		45·7	44·1	34·4	41·4		
While feeding Comfrey	July	15	47·8	44·0	36·4	42·7	77·0	59·0
		16	47·1	44·4	35·3	42·3	79·0	59·0
		17	49·9	42·5	36·4	42·9	77·0	63·0
		18	49·1	45·1	36·6	43·6	73·0	63·0
		19	47·2	42·6	38·0	42·6	75·0	62·0
		20	47·1	44·0	39·6	43·6	77·0	63·0
		21	47·1	42·0	36·4	41·8	87·0	63·0
	Average		47·9	43·5	37·0	42·8		
After Feeding	July	22	45·5	44·0	35·3	41·6	87·0	63·0
		23	44·5	42·0	33·0	39·8	88·0	63·0
		24	45·0	42·2	33·2	40·1	86·0	62·0
		25	44·5	44·2	32·8	40·5	86·0	63·0
		26	45·6	42·6	33·0	40·4	64·0	59·0
		27	43·0	40·5	33·2	38·9	84·0	64·0
		28	45·3	44·5	30·8	40·2	79·0	67·0
	Average		44·8	42·9	33·0	40·2		
Comfrey	July	29	46·5	41·0	31·5	39·7	88·0	59·5
		30	43·6	42·2	32·0	39·3	90·0	63·0
		31	44·6	42·0	29·6	38·7	92·0	65·5
	August	1	44·0	40·1	30·4	38·2	89·0	63·0
		2	42·6	41·6	33·5	39·2	89·0	64·5
		3	42·4	42·9	33·2	39·5	89·0	62·0
		4	44·2	40·5	31·2	38·6	87·0	73·5
	Average		44·0	41·5	31·6	39·0		

so the calves can pull it down as it is wanted without treading it to waste, and its advantages of a generous mineral supply when this is urgent for building bones are added to those of banishing scour risk.

The future, with cake prices rising constantly, and the value of barley for beer rather than beef feeding, could be one where extra cheap protein in silage and cut fodder will be valued. So many cows today never set hoof on grass, and all their material is cut and carried to them. Comfrey may well pay in these circumstances, but those who keep cattle under factory farm conditions usually prefer to owe money to a compounder rather than experiment with growing feed.

Mrs. P. B. Greer fed comfrey to her bullocks, in dry years when her pastures were poor, and at Mtoroshanga in Rhodesia, Mr. J. P. Phillips has fed the produce of the second largest comfrey field in the world to bullocks also. This twenty-five-acre plot, in cut all the year round, has been fattening bought-in stock for slaughter at about thirty months for Salisbury market for over seventeen years. The balance of the diet varies with the season, but generally speaking, the bullocks clear ¾ cwt. of comfrey a day. The only problem is drought, for though comfrey can draw on subsoil moisture, Rhodesian droughts can go on for years, and some form of emergency irrigation is desirable in all tropical countries. Three years without rain can kill comfrey, which Gerard described as 'joying in watery ditches'.

In Kenya, Mr. John McInnes used cut comfrey as his standard fodder for his Jersey herd, in an area where there is very little grazing in the dry season. His extra starch-equivalent material varied through the year, with maize straw, kikuyu grass, and even the thatch from condemned native huts in the year the long rains failed. His record yield in that year was cut and witnessed by some of the 250 visitors he had to his farm coming for miles to see the new crop that saved his herd. His phrase that 'comfrey kept two cows in milk where one starved before' was widely quoted, and coming from the Secretary of the Kenya Milk Recording Scheme, it did much to put comfrey on the map—until the pyrethrum eelworm destroyed his crop.

In 1958, the Grassland Research Department of Kenya published 'A Comparison between Russian Comfrey and Lucerne' (*East African Agricultural Journal*, January 1959) which gave yields of dry matter for lucerne of up to 43·60 cwt. an acre, which compares with the 36 cwt. in an 18 ton an acre record crop in England. This was compared with a comfrey yield of 37·87, which is less than the 45 cwt. dry matter in a 20 ton an acre British crop.

In the report it is mentioned that 'The Comfrey was infested with root eelworm'. Therefore the figures given can only be compared with quoting the crop from a field infested with potato eelworm as evidence that this crop is not worth growing either. They do not measure the yield, merely how *bad the eelworm was*. It is this kind of careless disregard for facts known to every good farmer who grows the crop well which makes research station figures on comfrey often misleading. Unfortunately once published in a reputable journal whose editor knows nothing about comfrey either, misleading figures are quoted all round the world, often by those who copy other men's references from the ends of their papers, and have never seen the crop in the field.

Just as the high figures quoted by comfrey sellers should be viewed with scepticism, the low ones given by authority deserve equal suspicion. It is likely that bad husbandry is hiding behind the brief and undetailed prose, especially in the summary in English at the end of a paper in Polish or German. A classic example is that of the plot at the Hannah Dairy Research Institute, which is often quoted.

The article 'Prickly Comfrey' by W. Holmes, B.Sc., N.D.A., N.D.D., appeared in *Agriculture* for February 1956, and it includes the following passages:

'The claims made for the plant (*Symphytum asperrimum*, with small blue flowers) were based on this sort of analysis figures and reports in the improvement in the health of unthrifty animals after being fed on the wilted leaves.

'They were not supported by the first-hand experience at the Hannah Institute farm, where a half-acre plot has been grown for several years. The rather upright growth of the plant and the necessity for fairly frequent cutting to provide young leafy herbage, prevent it covering the ground rapidly, and as a crop, therefore, it is rather difficult to establish and liable to serious weed infestation. The two most successful methods of establishment proved to be in rows two feet apart, and close-planted and inter-sown with Italian rye grass. With the first method cleaning may be done with row-crop equipment, with the second, the grass fills the spaces and weed growth is smothered. Once established, the crop comes into growth early in the spring and, when cut at regular intervals, continues to yield fresh leafy herbage until the first severe frost.

Yields of Green Comfrey
(*88 per cent moisture*)

1943	9 tons
1944	12 tons
1945	8 tons

'To summarize, as a summer silage crop, comfrey is less productive than, for instance, cereal-legume mixtures, and with the methods and equipment at present available it is unsuited for preservation for winter use. Owing to its very limited value for feeding purposes and the difficulties associated with its management and utilization, it is doubtful whether its cultivation on any considerable scale would be worth while.'

In correspondence with the writer, who sent a photograph of one of the Southery plants just ready for a 10 lb. cut, 4 feet high and 4 feet across, Mr. Holmes gave the following supplementary information:

'The plants were supplied by the late Kenneth Crawley in 1942 to Dr. Fowler, who was then in charge of the department. The land was not good but not poor, it had previously produced 16 tons of cabbage an acre and the crop received at least one heavy dressing of dung during its life. In 1945 the first cut of the four taken per season was 30 cwt. from the half-acre on April 20th and 28 cwt. on May 30th; the balance of the 8 tons was made up on the cuts July 13th and October 6th. Only in the July cut were any flower stems seen. It is not known exactly how much of the crop was clean-cultivated and how much under rye grass, and the plot is now ploughed up and its blue flowered descendants remain as weeds.'

It is quite clear from the article and the correspondence that the plant involved is not a hybrid comfrey, but the species *S. asperrimum*. It appears to have been unmanured and an unmeasured proportion of the plot was in grass, which is fatal to any worthwhile yield. No other crop would be written on in such a vague way in an official publication of the Ministry of Agriculture. The yield of any crop depends on how well it is grown and how much the farmer concerned knows of its cultivation and it would therefore be possible to establish that potatoes, in grass and without manure, were not worth growing, if they had the same official treatment.

Comfrey for Goats

No one has ever calculated starch equivalent in terms of what goats can use as 'digestible fibre'. They are bush and bark eaters because of their need for minerals, and though the modern dairy goat is as productive in terms of body weight as a Jersey cow, it must have the roughage to go with the grass and protein that keeps up the milk yield.

Through the years of war and rationing, Mrs. P. B. Greer supplied goats' milk for ice cream and other uses to London hotels, and, as a 'now-it-can-be-told' story, she sold her surplus billy kids to the Savoy Hotel and the chefs there worked wonders with this unrationed meat. Now there is a steadily increasing demand for yoghourt, and goats' milk makes this in the very best quality, so once again the goat has a specialized and expanding market waiting for its produce.

Goats need protein as well as roughage, and though they were reputed to supply milk for the captain's children on sailing ships from a diet of old log books and worn out rope, they need better food than that for a commercial milk yield. Comfrey provides a very good source of protein and minerals for goats, and it can be fed in winter as roof-top hay, to go with a high roughage diet. The amount that can be fed each day depends on the individual goat, but it has been observed that there is a curve that can be plotted on the milk chart. Up to a limit there is an increase in yield as the amount of comfrey fed goes up, then it falls sharply, because comfrey is high protein and low fibre and goats need that fibre.

Comfrey is not a complete diet for anything, and attempts to use it as a sole source of protein will fail, but it is a useful bulk source of cheap protein which can be substituted for more expensive

foods, or used to upgrade a poor diet. It is cheaper to supply the
minerals that goats need in comfrey than to grow trees for them to
bark, and to feed their roughage as a high cellulose material such as
barley straw.

Comfrey for Sheep and other animals

Sheep were stall-fed on comfrey in Ireland in the nineteenth
century, but no details are available of the ration and this extraordinary system would be completely uneconomic today. It has
been used in Wales in corners near the farmyard as a source of very
early high protein food cut hard in spring, and again in the autumn
when pastures grow poor.

At Carnew Castle, *Symphytum asperrimum* was the sole diet of
working donkeys, and an H.D.R.A. member, Major Linton, who
farmed on the east-facing slopes of the Andes, used Bocking No. 14
which he smuggled out in the early days of our trial ground, as
food for both mules and donkeys. His vines grew on steep terraces
where no tractor could work and comfrey provided the concentrated protein to produce the 'bean effect' in increasing pull. The
extra rail charges imposed in the early 1960s made it uneconomic
to send the wine into the Argentine and the best market was
smugglers from Peru. Their animals were given a comfrey supper
and breakfast before they started their long journey via mountain
paths with a barrel on each side of their pack saddles, like the
'four and twenty ponies, trotting through the dark' along the lanes
of Old England.

In 1962, Whipsnade Zoo bought enough comfrey for about $2\frac{1}{2}$
acres from the trial ground, and Mr. H. Tong, the then curator,
fed it to elephants, hippopotami, rhinoceroses and giraffes, which
were the animals that broke in and stole it most often from the
farms of growers in Kenya and Rhodesia. This is a tribute to the
nutritional wisdom of wild animals.

Giraffes have very much more weight on their legs than race
horses, and their cannon-bones must be much harder. They too
must graze for speed and minerals, and they obtain the last from
twigs and small branches, reaching far higher than other animals,
and using their long, blue-grey tongues to wrap round the branches

and strip off both leaves and bark. They can graze by spreading their forelegs and this is mainly how they feed at Whipsnade, but they appreciate comfrey thrown on their pastures or offered as a tit-bit.

In 1963 I visited Whipsnade and went round with Mr. Tong to see his animals eat a shooting-brakeful of cut comfrey. We stopped by a shaded pool and Mr. Tong called 'Henry', but there was no movement from what looked like a large sack of tar. Again he called, this time more sharply 'Henry, come *here*', and this time Henry rose and opened up to receive a generous ration of comfrey. A hippo is a distant relation of the pig, and normally takes a great deal of exercise. If he is fed a diet rich in carbohydrate, instead of the water lily and aquatic plant feeding, varied with robbery from native gardens, he can put on weight. Comfrey, which is high protein and high mineral, is the equivalent to a slimming food for hippos who must count their calories.

It was fed also to Mohima, a cow rhino with a new-born calf, which was smooth and chestnut brown, and Dixie, an elephant with forty years' experience of taking children round Regent's Park Zoo before transfer to Whipsnade. An elephant will eat at least a hundredweight of comfrey a day, because it is also a highly suitable diet. Elephants cannot graze, and their trunks are their feeding 'limbs'. They will root up a shrub or young tree, dust the soil off its roots on their knees and put it in their mouths like a man eating asparagus. They may kneel and use their tusks to loosen a shrub of a kind they fancy, and can even dig out roots, as well as tearing up plants and grasses to eat by the trunkful. Comfrey appears to suit them very well, without causing them to put on too much weight—an advantage for animals in captivity. The farmer needs liveweight increase and milk yield, the zoo curator would like his charges to keep much as they are, reaching the happy state of 'I don't worry about this slimming business. What I always say is, "a little bit of what you fancy does you good".' And that seemed to apply at Whipsnade too.

The plot at Whipsnade has now been ploughed up and grassed down and has died out except for a few hedgerow survivals. Mr. Tong retired, and his successor considered comfrey remarkably subject to frost, since it died down in November. He had hoped that it would be a winter substitute for the kales which many animals dislike, but of course it goes dormant in winter. It had been planted by his predecessor purely as a summer feed to give a cheap, in terms of labour, and nutritious diet supplement in summer, and, as always, when management changes, comfrey is neglected. No cuts were ever weighed from this large planting, which is a pity for it would have been interesting to see what kind of yields were achieved on elephant manure.

Those who run zoos are often short of space, and a comfrey plot could be the answer to the summer green food problem for animals with digestions that fit comfrey. As with chinchillas and racehorses, however, the object is not money-saving but giving valued stock the best possible diet, and therefore comfrey should be grown well, but tried and discarded if it fails. Pigs can only be run on comfrey until their snouts harden for rooting, and this goes for wart hogs too.

8. Comfrey in the garden

In the twenty-five years through which I have grown comfrey, the greatest development in its cultivation has been in the garden especially, by what are called 'organic gardeners' in Britain and America—an ever increasing army of whom I am one.

We do not use persistent chemical pesticides, fungicides or herbicides, preferring substances of vegetable origin which do not build up resistant populations of pests and spare the predators which are natural pest controllers. The problems which many garden chemicals increase or replace with worse, we solve by applied ecology and biology, which may mean a need for greater knowledge, but our answers *last* rather than build up pollution and long-term trouble for the future.

We do not use chemical fertilizers either, for reasons concerned with nutrition, flavour and conservation, for we look even further ahead than the man who plants a walnut tree and waits fifteen years for his first nuts. Like the good farmers to whom we owe the fertile acres of England, we think of those who will garden and farm when we lie under the land we used to plough. Mining the limited number of dried seabeds from the past which left us potash deposits, or massive dead fish kills, like the geological disaster which gave us North African rock phosphate, and converting them to rapidly soluble fertilizers which wash from the soil into the great sink of the sea can exhaust in a century what should keep us fed on fertile farms through eons of time.

An oakwood or a tropical forest is what ecologists call a 'climax' —a balance of income from the living leaves and the life which depends on them which can circle through the sunlit years in harmony. Man can be part of that climax. Industrial Man is a catastrophe—the terminal disease of a sickened planet. That is my opinion.

I am an ecologist, a conservationist and an organic gardener, so, unlike a politician, I cannot think only as far as the next election, and to those who say 'what has the future done for me?', I say 'look what the men of the past have done for us all, and try to leave your land more fertile than you found it'.

Let us consider the difference between an organic and an inorganic fertilizer, between the potash in comfrey foliage, in wood ashes, and, say, the potassium chloride (still called 'Muriate of Potash') from the Stassfurt deposits in Germany or the Dead Sea in Israel.

Experiments at the University of Saskatchewan in the early 1950s, using radioactive tracers, have shown that plants only take up between 2 and 6 per cent of the plant-food minerals in theory available to them. When a crop with radioactive molecules in it was fed to stock, it was found that this had taken up the plant foods in the manure almost completely, because all the molecules were originally selected by the roots of a plant. Every molecule in your body and mine was chosen by the root hairs of a plant, or, if it came from fish in the sea, by one of the tiny floating plants called 'plankton' which power everything from shrimps to whales, and fuel the mighty albatross on its long and lonely flights.

When you apply 2 oz. a square yard of potassium chloride, 94 per cent washes down into the soil, and that 2 or 6 per cent is taken up by your plants. This is fine, so long as supplies last and there are no other complications. That idle potassium in your soil will stop your plants taking up magnesium, another vital plant food, and most gardeners have seen its effect in the tomato bed, where the lower leaves turn yellow but the veins stay green. When you put on compost, or manure, which have all their molecules root-selected, there is no problem—the crops manage on that 2 per cent passed from 'hand to hand' by the soil bacteria and fungi, into plants, and back again to the soil.

What about the wood ashes? These are a mixture of a number of chemicals, and their potash is mainly potassium carbonate, altered completely from the original root-selected molecules which appear to be potassium sulphate in comfrey. Wood ashes are simply a collection of inorganic chemicals, like Kainite, which is salts from a dried-up seabed of the remote past, containing potassium chloride, plus sodium chloride and magnesium chloride. Fire was Man's first fertilizer factory and it made deserts before men made chemicals.

When trees grow, they store away in wood the potash and other plant foods which they take in through their roots, going far down to find the molecules which their secretions make available. These are locked away so tightly that they can only be released by fire, or the bacteria like Hutchinson's spirochaete which can break down hard celluloses and hemicelluloses.

Think of these plant foods as savings, tucked away in Local Government loans which pay good interest but cannot be touched for years. Comfrey, however, keeps all its mineral gatherings on current account, ready for instant use. Its roots go down to small-tree depths and a comfrey bed is a mineral mine for plants, just as a large plot on a stud farm gathers the calcium for the strong bones of foals trying a first gallop round the paddock in the sunshine, and a field on a pig farm provides the copper which prevents pig anaemia, by giving that 2 to 6 per cent in the food, instead of passing over 90 per cent out in the dung to build metal toxicity in the soil.

When we make compost we are using bacteria to lower its proportion of carbon to nitrogen compounds and produce heat. With ordinary garden rubbish, the proportion of C to N is about 80 to 1, and in composting this should come down to near 10 to 1, which still leaves enough power to 'drive' the soil fungi, bacteria and earthworms. Mostly the bacteria of decay break down the starches and sugars plus some of the cellulose. Comfrey, however, has so little fibre and so much protein, that its carbon to nitrogen ratio is about 14 to 1, so in theory it is compost before it goes on the heap.

I made my first all-comfrey compost in 1955 with some of the first cuts on the new H.D.R.A. trial ground, and a whole heap about four feet high smashed down to about six inches, composed of the fibres and a black and tarry looking mess, that was mainly broken down proteins. It looked like cowdung, and was such a good imitation, that a number of the pale rusty red flies which live on cow pats gathered and began to feed.

I learned then that the only way to make good compost with comfrey was to mix it in with other ingredients, just like making silage, gaining the quick heating from the starches and sugars and the extra potash to enrich the heap. Then in 1956 I tried treating comfrey foliage as a kind of 'Instant Compost', using it at the rate of $1\frac{1}{2}$ lb. a foot of row, which doubled the yield of potatoes compared with the 'no-manure' plots, and ever since then the experiment has been repeated every year on the trial ground. This is the kind of yield achieved.

1960 POTATO TRIAL

Manure	Comfrey	Compost
54 lb.	69 lb.	77 lb.
Comfrey	Compost	Manure
71 lb.	63 lb.	74 lb.
Compost	Manure	Comfrey
54 lb.	50 lb.	73 lb.

Total compost 194 lb., total manure 178 lb., total comfrey 213 lb.

The 1971 experiment, on a different plot, compares comfrey, compost and chemicals in the same way.

On 13 February three barrows of compost were 'Merrytilled' into the three compost squares and $3\frac{1}{2}$ lb. of Growmore into the artificials. Our standard plots are 7 square yards, so this smallest size packet does each one exactly. On Saturday 1 May, we planted 20 seed tubers of Record on each square, with 1 lb. a foot of row of cut comfrey on the comfrey square and 2 lb. a foot on Square 3. We were late because a cold dry spring meant a slow start for everything.

On 11 September we dug and weighed the crop with the result shown on the facing page.

The plots in both experiments are 'replicated', repeated so that no two come next to each other, to cancel out variations in soil fertility, on what is called a 'Latin Square replication'. This is the simplest of all, and it means that three treatments need nine plots, four need sixteen and so on. There are many more complicated

Plot 7 : Compost			Plot 8 : Comfrey			Plot 9 : Growmore		
Row 1	5 lb.	4 oz.	Row 1	5 lb.	12 oz.	Row 1	5 lb.	2 oz.
Row 2	7 lb.	6 oz.	Row 2	9 lb.	14 oz.	Row 2	6 lb.	14 oz.
Row 3	7 lb.	6 oz.	Row 3	8 lb.	14 oz.	Row 3	7 lb.	2 oz.
Row 4	8 lb.	8 oz.	Row 4	6 lb.	10 oz.	Row 4	7 lb.	12 oz.
Total:	28 lb.	8 oz.	Total:	31 lb.	2 oz.	Total:	26 lb.	14 oz.

Plot 4 : Comfrey			Plot 5 : Growmore			Plot 6 : Compost		
Row 1	10 lb.	4 oz.	Row 1	7 lb.	12 oz.	Row 1	12 lb.	2 oz.
Row 2	12 lb.	8 oz.	Row 2	8 lb.	14 oz.	Row 2	10 lb.	8 oz.
Row 3	13 lb.	2 oz.	Row 3	8 lb.	4 oz.	Row 3	12 lb.	1 oz.
Row 4	8 lb.	6 oz.	Row 4	8 lb.	9 oz.	Row 4	9 lb.	10 oz.
Total:	44 lb.	4 oz.	Total:	33 lb.	7 oz.	Total:	44 lb.	5 oz.

Plot 1 : Growmore			Plot 2 : Compost			Plot 3 : Comfrey		
Row 1	12 lb.	14 oz.	Row 1	12 lb.	4 oz.	Row 1	15 lb.	12 oz.
Row 2	10 lb.	10 oz.	Row 2	13 lb.	1 oz.	Row 2	15 lb.	10 oz.
Row 3	9 lb.	7 oz.	Row 3	11 lb.	10 oz.	Row 3	13 lb.	6 oz.
Row 4	13 lb.	9 oz.	Row 4	10 lb.	4 oz.	Row 4	13 lb.	2 oz.
Total:	46 lb.	8 oz.	Total:	47 lb.	3 oz.	Total:	57 lb.	14 oz.

Totals: Comfrey   ..   .. 133 lb. 4 oz.
Compost ..   .. 120 lb. 0 oz.
Growmore ..   .. 106 lb. 13 oz.

replications used on large research stations, but this one is the easiest for amateurs. It will be noticed that all the plots towards the top of the page are low and those at the bottom run higher, so if the Growmore had been put at the top and the compost at the bottom the result would have merely measured the difference in the fertility, not in the treatments.

The Growmore squares have had nothing but chemicals for three years, and in a dry season the lack of the moisture-retaining power from the missing humus shows in a reduced yield. The crop is very much what can be expected from the following table:

	Water per cent	Nitrogen per cent	Phos- phorus per cent	Potash per cent	C-N Ratio
Farmyard manure	76·0	0·64	0·23	0·32	14–1
Russian comfrey (wilted)	75·0	0·74	0·24	1·19	9·8–1
Indore compost	76·0	0·5	0·27	0·81	10–1
Municipal compost (Edinburgh)	49·4	0·77	0·06	0·09	—
Comfrey compost	68·0	0·77	0·29	0·92	

Wilted comfrey has more than twice as much potash as good farmyard manure and about 30 per cent more than compost, though the last varies according to what goes into it, and the last figures in the table are from a heap made with about 20 per cent comfrey. The C-N ratio is lower, because the comfrey was cut at the leafy stage, not stemmy and running to flower with more fibre. The wilting is because when cut comfrey is left overnight it is flabby enough to pack neatly in the potato trenches and it reduces the risk of thick stems growing as cuttings where they are unwanted. Comfrey Bocking No. 14 is the favourite garden variety partly because its small and slender stems wilt most easily and are least likely to grow in the trench.

Comfrey cut for compost means 8 to 10 barrowloads wheeled for every barrow of finished compost. General garden rubbish runs 5 to 6 barrows to one, but wilted comfrey produces three barrows of material of the above analysis for every four cut. This is a bargain in organic plant foods for space and trouble, with no compost bin to make, no activator, no turning and no waiting. There are no weed seeds either, for comfrey should always be cut regularly so there is no chance for the plants to waste strength on attempting to set seeds.

It has the drawback that with so little fibre it cannot leave much humus in the ground. There are just some black remains and none of the accumulation which compost provides, but it offers organic plant foods as a 'grow-it-yourself' general fertilizer, to make compost go further, and the art of using it through the season for crops that need most potash has become part of organic gardening.

The Majestic potatoes grown in the 1960 trial were tested for flavour by 28 H.D.R.A. members, who received four sets of samples under letters only. For statistical purposes this was far too few, but it was at least as accurate as a 'blindfold test' for whisky.

Firstly it appears that the one person who put the chemically grown Majestic first on flavour was a smoker. Only four people, all of them meat eaters, placed it second and a resounding seventeen volunteers accorded it last place. In contrast, potatoes grown with comfrey were the first choice of no less than sixteen members out

FIRST PREFERENCE

Taster	A Comfrey	B FYM	C Compost	D Chemicals	Total
Vegan Non-smoker	2	—	—	—	2
Vegetarian Non-smoker	5	—	—	—	5
Meat Eater ⎰ Smoker	4	1	2	1	8
⎱ Non-smoker	5	6	2	—	13
Total	16	7	4	1	28

SECOND PREFERENCE

Taster	A Comfrey	B FYM	C Compost	D Chemicals	Total
Vegan Non-smoker	—	2	—	—	2
Vegetarian Non-smoker	—	—	5	—	5
Meat Eater ⎰ Smoker	—	5	2	1	8
⎱ Non-smoker	—	6	4	3	13
Total	—	13	11	4	28

THIRD PREFERENCE

Taster	A Comfrey	B FYM	C Compost	D Chemicals	Total
Vegan Non-smoker	—	—	—	2	2
Vegetarian Non-smoker	—	5	—	—	5
Meat Eater ⎰ Smoker	2	2	4	—	8
⎱ Non-smoker	2	1	6	4	13
Total	4	8	10	6	28

FOURTH PREFERENCE

Taster	A Comfrey	B FYM	C Compost	D Chemicals	Total
Vegan Non-smoker	—	—	2	—	2
Vegetarian Non-smoker	—	—	—	5	5
Meat Eater ⎰ Smoker	2	—	—	6	8
⎱ Non-smoker	6	—	1	6	13
Total	8	—	3	17	28

of twenty-eight. This included all seven of the vegetarian and
vegan voters. Manure (pig and cow F.Y.M.) rated seven firsts,
thirteen seconds and eight thirds, while compost (weeds and
comfrey with a manure activator) scored four firsts, eleven
seconds, ten thirds and three fourths. The resulting picture is of a
taste that the majority found best—comfrey, and a tastelessness
that most put last—chemicals. Compost and farmyard manure
came in between.

The site for a comfrey bed should always be in full sun and
away from trees or a privet hedge, for the more the comfrey is
manured, the faster these roots will rob it. It needs sun to keep its
great leaves swallowing the sunlight and pumping the water up
through its roots to split into oxygen and hydrogen, to make the
carbo-*hydrates* that begin the leaf chemistry on which all life
depends.

As on the farm, it does best on a clay, dislikes thin soils over
rock, and on light sands and loams, including the soot and broken
glass mixtures of city centres, it will thrive, but needs plenty of
manure. Choose the comfrey bed site and stick to it, but if it is to
be moved or extended, use the methods described in Chapter 5.
The only difference on a garden scale is that a two foot apart each
way spacing means that the plants crowd together faster and
reduce the need for weeding.

Plant deeply so that growing points are just below the surface on
ground which has been well cleared of perennial weeds. A comfrey
bed will last as long as your fruit trees, and therefore it pays to
take considerable trouble in preparing the ground, using ammonium sulphamate if you have any really fierce weeds. In a
garden, summer plantings are possible even in July and August,
because the new bed can be watered more easily than a field, and
this gives a chance to put on the ammonium sulphamate when the
weeds are growing strongly in April. Wait six weeks, then plant
with time for your bed to be well established for a full cutting
season next year. Do not try to cut it in the first year if it is late
planted, but let the foliage die down on it, as you would with
rhubarb.

The first summer the plants will need hoeing as seedling weeds germinate, and after that, if possible, keep it fed with deep litter manure or mushroom compost mulches. A comfrey bed is in effect a method of exchanging crude nitrogen for a balanced organic fertilizer and so it can have poultry manure straight off the dropping boards, dried sewage sludge, or the mixture of two parts water to one of urine which is known to H.D.R.A. members as 'H.L.A.' or Household Liquid Activator because it is the best and cheapest of all compost heap activators.

The analysis of all dried sludges and municipal composts has the potash as 'trace' or '·oo1', because men, unlike chickens, pass their urine as a liquid and this goes down to the sea in effluent, growing nothing but unwanted blanket weed on the way. On the comfrey bed it is as good as it is in the compost heap. As on the farm, it is wasteful to put compost on the comfrey bed where it cannot release enough nitrogen to grow the crop at full speed, but H.L.A., if it can be spared, provides both potash and nitrogen. In all my years of comfrey growing, I have never seen a good crop that was fed with chemical nitrogen, though in theory, nitro-chalk (calcium nitrate) is ideal. It is in fact the research stations who insist on feeding it chemically who often have the lowest yields.

Another excellent comfrey manure and compost heap activator is pigeon manure, which holds about 6 per cent nitrogen, 2·50 per cent phosphorus, 2·30 per cent potash and 1·80 per cent calcium which is about six times F.Y.M. nitrogen, three times the phosphorus and five times the potash. There are about 200,000 pigeon keepers in Britain (or were in 1965) and the few who garden as well as follow their hobby, which involves far more people than hunting, know that this is far too strong to use. Poultry manure is bad enough at forcing potatoes ahead to all top and no tubers, and growing sprouting broccoli too tall and soft to stand the winter, but pigeon manure is worse.

However, comfrey will take it. Scatter the droppings between the rows, ideally in showery weather or when you can hose the bed, and the plants will leap ahead. If you can find your local pigeon club, many members will be glad to get rid of their manure. Look in your local paper, or write to *The Racing Pigeon*, 19 Doughty Street, London W.C.1. Hoard it in a dry shed and use it in layers not more than half an inch thick in your compost heap, or to feed your comfrey bed.

Just as on a farm, the three secrets of comfrey growing are 'Keep it clean, keep it cut, keep it fed', with the difference that unless you are feeding it to poultry you do not need to cut it every day. The aim is still between four and five cuts a year, but these are spaced to fit the needs of the garden through the season. An example of the kind of yield one can expect from an established comfrey bed of a dozen plants is the following 1960 trial from Mr. Harold Kirkman of Southport, who grows Bocking No. 14.

18 April	18 lb.
5 June	88 lb.
24 July	52 lb.
18 September	63 lb.
	221 lb.

The yield per acre is merely to compare with the earlier farm figures. What is important is the $1\frac{1}{2}$ cwt. or so of high potash organic general fertilizer he grew. It is likely that a gardener who gave his comfrey bed the attention and feeding which some gardeners give their carnations could reach the hundred tons an acre even in Britain. In terms of fertility it would be worth the effort.

The early start which Bocking No. 14 gives is important, but the first cut must always go for the potatoes, and it is wanted sooner than it is ready. There are many ways round the problem, and the system on the H.D.R.A. trial ground is to leave the main-crops or earlies in the chitting trays, standing 'rose end' (the one where the eyes are) up until late April or even May, when there should be plenty of comfrey for them.

We then take out potato trenches to a full fork's depth and spread 1 to $1\frac{1}{2}$ lb. of wilted comfrey to every foot of row. Some gardeners put an inch of soil on top of the comfrey, but we often just set the seed tubers a foot apart for earlies, fifteen inches for maincrop, straight on the comfrey, then spade the soil back over them, leaving a ridge on the surface which marks the position of the rows. The distance between rows is the same, and the potatoes grow in what are, in effect, long, narrow compost heaps which release their plant foods as they are required. Some gardeners have always used lawn mowings in potato trenches to reduce scab damage by the acidity which the causative fungus (*Actinomyces scabies*) dislikes, but grass cuttings have only about 0·6 per cent potash and less nitrogen.

H.D.R.A. member Mr. Allan Thompson of Stinsford, found the most popular method of ensuring that there is enough comfrey for early potatoes. He planted his unsprouted Arran Banner on 2 April in furrows four inches deep, 30 inches apart and a foot between tubers. The whole plot had an unmeasured quantity of 12 per cent potash fishmeal (fishmeal with potassium chloride added) applied evenly when the ground was dug. All the rows were covered with fresh compost to keep the frost off the seed at planting time. When there was enough comfrey available, the comfrey rows were mulched with leaves left in the sun a few hours to wilt, spread over and between the rows just before earthing up to eight inches high. The compost rows had exactly the same treatment but with no comfrey.

The crop was lifted as most people lift earlies, as they are wanted for eating, with the following result; in every case eight plants with comfrey and eight without were lifted each time.

	Compost and comfrey		Compost only	
	lb.	oz.	lb.	oz.
14 July	11	8	3	14
18 July	9	12	4	1
20 July	10	11	5	13
21 July	11	12	5	14
23 July	11	10	7	15
30 July	15	0	8	0
30 July	13	$1\frac{1}{2}$	5	8
4 August	15	2	9	12
4 August	16	$4\frac{1}{2}$	7	12
4 August	13	2	7	4
4 August	15	2	6	14
13 August	15	14	9	8
Total from 96 tubers	158	15	82	3

The extra 77 lb. from using comfrey as well as compost was well worth the effort, especially as the difference was widest in the early weeks when new potatoes are at their most expensive. Another system was used by Mr. John Raimbach of Benfleet who reported:

'I don't bother to experiment with weight and taste now—I am convinced. In the past I have had to plant my earlies without comfrey since they miss the first cut, but this year I have laid my last comfrey cut on the site reserved for next year's early spuds. Over this I have laid a spread of strawy horse manure to remain in situ till next April. This solves the comfrey problem for earlies I hope. Incidentally I now make my best compost ever by adding a cut of comfrey when preparing a heap.'

This policy of spreading the last cut under manure, or grass mowings in September or October for earlies, is popular also for onion beds, for as the comfrey foliage rots under the mowings, the potash soaks down and the mowings to some extent at least, prevent winter weedgrowth and mineral leaching. Mr. Raimbach was on some particularly heavy clay, but he found comfrey on the surface plus his manure far better than leaving the ground 'rough dug for the frosts'. On a sand this system is still more useful.

The problem of onions is that sets have to be planted too late for the comfrey. In 1961 a trial was planted on 4 April, after tucking wilted comfrey in the trench bottoms as the onion bed was dug. The result was a total of 22 lb. for the comfrey and 15 lb. for the compost off the same area, which was not good for either, but the disturbance of the ground as the fresh comfrey sank, as well as the late planting, reduced the yield.

In September 1970 about a barrowload of wilted comfrey was dug into three squares of a bed of nine, seven-square-yard plots on the H.D.R.A. trial ground, a good barrowload of compost into three, and the last three had $3\frac{1}{2}$ lb. of Growmore chemical compound fertilizer. The squares are as far as possible standardized at this size for ease of working out cwts. and acres in calculating from them, and as this book is written for farmers and gardeners, not scientific workers or schools and universities, all measurements are non-metric. On 26 February 1971 the squares were all planted with onion sets which were lifted on 23 August with the following results:

Plot 7: Comfrey *best dozen (oz.)* 8, 7, 9, 11, 7½, 9, 6, 7½, 9, 10, 6½, 8½ Total: 17 lb. 8 oz.	*Plot 8: Growmore* *best dozen (oz.)* 3, 2½, 4, 4½, 4½, 5¼, 4¾, 3¼, 3½, 3½, 3¾, 4 Total: 7 lb. 12 oz.	*Plot 9: Compost* *best dozen (oz.)* 3½, 3¼, 3¾, 4¼, 4½, 4½, 3½, 3, 4¼, 3½, 4, 4½ Total: 12 lb. 12 oz
Plot 4: Compost *best dozen* 8½, 8¼, 8¼, 10, 12½, 7¼, 10¼, 11, 10½, 11¾, 7¼, 7½ Total: 18 lb. 0 oz.	*Plot 5: Comfrey* *best dozen* 7, 5, 5½, 5, 12½, 10, 10, 7, 7, 5¼, 6¾, 4½ Total: 12 lb. 0 oz.	*Plot 6: Growmore* *best dozen* 3½, 4½, 2¾, 3, 2¾, 3¼, 3¾, 3, 3½, 3½, 3½, 3, 4 Total: 10 lb. 8 oz.
Plot 1: Growmore *best dozen* 8, 8, 7, 9, 7½, 7½, 8¼, 6½, 6, 7, 7, 6½ Total: 12 lb. 8 oz.	*Plot 2: Compost* *best dozen* 5¼, 4½, 4, 4½, 5, 4½, 3, 2, 3, 3¾, 5¼, 3 Total: 16 lb. 0 oz.	*Plot 3: Comfrey* *best dozen* 8½, 10¾, 6, 12, 6½, 5¾, 5¾, 6½, 5¼, 7¼, 6¼, 8½ Total: 20 lb. 12 oz

Totals:		
	Comfrey	50 lb. 8 oz.
	Compost	46 lb. 12 oz.
	Growmore	30 lb. 12 oz.

Show onions are judged on size, and though housewives prefer small ones, judges like them large. Some gardeners buy costly sets of special strains such as Giant Fen, and others feed their soils with soot, salt and all kinds of esoteric mixtures to grow onions fit to cap Kremlin towers or grace the front at Brighton. Those who know their onions scorn even half pounders—nothing under 10 oz. is worthy of a condescending glance. So the onions in the trial were sorted over to find the largest with the following result:

Comfrey 10, 10, 10¾, 11, 12, 12½
Compost 10, 10¼, 10½, 11, 11¾, 12½
Growmore 8, 8, 8¼, 9

We have had 14 oz. specimens with comfrey, but 1961 was a poor year for onions. The Growmore is low, but no one growing onions for show would use it. Special high potash manures are usually employed.

The last comfrey cut that comes in for the onions is also useful for broad beans, autumn-sown to dodge the black fly, because unless these have a generous supply of potash, they are attacked by the chocolate spot fungus. Using chemical fertilizer, potassium on a sandy soil can mean that this is all washed out by the spring when the need is greatest. In September 1960 we divided our bean trenches into three sections each 14 feet long. One had 30 lb. of wilted comfrey, another had about the same bulk of farmyard manure and the third section had nothing. There were three rows, to give the same pattern as the potato and onion trials, and they were sown with Seville Long Pod on 16 November.

They were up on 24 December 1960, flowered first on 14 April and we started picking on 26 May. The comfrey sections yielded 29 lb. in 319 pods, the manure sections 19 lb. 4 oz. in 359 pods and the 'nothings' 6 lb. 14 oz. in 184 pods. The extra potash from the comfrey grew rather fewer, but larger pods, the manure looked just as good plants, while the 'nothings' got chocolate spot and looked very poor.

Runner and french beans are sown or planted from boxes later than potatoes, and therefore they can fit the second comfrey cut. In 1961 we used the same replication, with 30 lb. of wilted comfrey in three sections, compared with three of manure and three of nothing—the trenches were just opened and filled again. The variety was Hammonds Dwarf Scarlet, the bush kind, and 14 seeds were sown to each section, on 16 May. They were up on 5 June, flowered first on 12 July and had pods on the 19th. The 'nothing' sections yielded 16 lb. 2 oz., the compost 31 lb. 8 oz. and the comfrey 43 lb. 5 oz.

This 'bush' runner does not stand high on a stout stem, but flops, so the effect is of a short scarlet runner lying on the ground like an ordinary runner bean grown by farmers. The pods curve and lie muddy on the soil, for they are much heavier than french bean pods and really need the support of short sticks or canes. The cut comfrey was trodden into the trenches because these behave like long narrow 'compost heaps' and there is sinkage as they decay.

There have been many attempts to use this bean trench system to grow tomatoes with comfrey in the foot square and deep planting holes that normally hold compost when the crop is grown in the open. The difficulty is that the foliage decays and sinks, breaking the tomato roots, and therefore the liquid manure described later is the best method of using the potash in comfrey to feed tomatoes. Another system is to spread the cut foliage between the rows as a weed-suppressing mulch which will release some potash as it is trodden down with picking and trimming, but most stays on the surface to be dug or rotavated in, and provides potash for the November broad bean sowing that avoids black fly. This also serves for the Tic and Daffa beans that can be dried for concentrated protein, and prevents the chocolate spot that they can suffer from if they run out of potash.

This is the standard way of using comfrey between bush fruit, especially for gooseberries which are always potash-hungry on sandy soils. Spread as much cut comfrey as can be spared at any time during the summer, in a 2-inch thick layer when it is wilted, with 2 to 3 inches of lawn mowings on too to prevent drying and hasten breakdown on a kind of sheet composting system. The signs of potash shortage in gooseberries are grey brown margins to the leaves, with a purple tint in the middles and small and few fruit. If enough comfrey is available it can go between both raspberries and blackcurrants, the last gaining the nitrogen, but not in the excess that makes the bushes 'put on too much weight' for small gardens.

Comfrey liquid manure was invented by an early H.D.R.A. member, Mr. George Gibson of Guernsey, who grew a comfrey bed solely for feeding his greenhouse tomatoes when they began setting their first trusses. The usual procedure is to fill a water butt about quarter full of comfrey leaves and stems, top up with water and draw off the result, but in May 1973 I made some with more care, as an experiment. I had a 20 gallon fibreglass rainwater butt and propped it up on an old galvanized water tank, so it was well clear of the ground to allow cans to be pushed under the tap for filling. This we filled by hose and then added 14 lb. of fresh cut comfrey leaves, which filled up to quite a bulk. The lid of the water butt was replaced, and the hole in it covered with a large tin lid.

The comfrey went black quite quickly and formed a kind of crust on the surface, on which small flies ran. After a month we tried the first canfuls on the frame tomatoes as they were setting their blossom and later on the main outdoor plants. More water and comfrey leaves were added later, for the aim was simply to make a good organic tonic for tomato plants. Anyone who grows comfrey in his garden can afford to be generous with it in his manure tub.

The results were analysed by the Michaelis Nutritional Laboratory, comparing comfrey liquid manure with Tomorite made according to the directions as a standard mainly inorganic plant food, and Marinure as an organic seaweed feed, also made up to the directions.

	Tomorite *per cent*	*Marinure* *per cent*	*Comfrey* *per cent*
Dry matter	0·1410	0·0480	0·4090
Nitrogen	0·0130	0·0070	0·0140
Potash	0·0139	0·0019	0·0340
Phosphorus	0·0093	0·0001	0·0059

The comfrey was, of course, much stronger than the others in terms of dry matter, but it will be noted that while the chemical mixture had roughly as much nitrogen as potash and about a third less phosphorus, the comfrey had roughly three times as much potash as nitrogen, and far less phosphorus, which is the balance of plant food tomatoes need. This liquid feed could be used for pot plants and for general garden purposes, with runner beans gaining from the potash almost as much as tomatoes. Mr. Gibson considered that it was wasteful to compost comfrey because so much of the potash seeped away below the heap, but forking it into the tanks outside every greenhouse preserved it all. The residue is quite good compost, and as the water butt gets low it can be tipped out and dug in. Some gardeners top up with more water, which reduces the strength of the liquid, but 14 lb. to 20 gallons is a good nutrient level for tomatoes.

A development for the future is as a fill for methane gas plants, for with 9·8 to 1 carbon-nitrogen ratio there is almost as much nitrogen as in poultry manure, which makes it possible to achieve the 25 to 1 for efficient methane production by adding lawn mowings and other green vegetable or weed wastes. The resulting liquid would contain all the plant foods, but still as the root selected molecules with which we began. This might well be the key to domestic methane generators, cutting the fuel costs for the homes of the future, and providing fertility by the canful for small gardens in an age not of leisure but ever higher food prices.

9. Comfrey for human food

In Britain and the U.S.A. a great many gardeners eat comfrey as a spinach-like vegetable, slightly bitter in flavour and best picked small when the leaves are not more than six inches long. This is not the way to secure maximum yield, but those who have half-a-dozen plants often cut one back hard for compost, or liquid manure, and pick this continually for a fortnight, then let it grow and change over to another one. Others let the leaves grow larger, but the stems are too stringy for normal eating. The following recipes have been worked out through the years by members of the H.D.R.A.

Fresh Comfrey as a Green Vegetable

Pick the leaves, wash them, shake off the surplus water and put straight into a dry enamel saucepan where the wet on the leaves and their juice is usually enough to cook them tender in ten minutes, with the lid on over a low gas or electric hot-plate setting. If there seems too little water add a tablespoonful or so, but boiling—as with cabbage—wastes protein and destroys the flavour, which is a blend of endive and asparagus.

Another way of cooking comfrey spinach fashion is the following Chinese recipe modified for the West.

1) Collect a basketful of comfrey leaves.
2) Get a saucepan ready and put in the bottom a knob of margarine, or vegetable oil.
3) Wash and cut approximately a quarter of the leaves into manageable sizes.
4) Light low gas under saucepan, and drop in prepared leaves.
5) Wash and cut remaining leaves and as they are cut drop them into the saucepan, where the first leaves will have shrunk and exuded enough juice to render the use of water unnecessary.

6) Add salt to taste.
7) Cook gently for 8 to 10 minutes.
8) Serve as for cabbage.

Fresh Comfrey and Nettle Soup

About 12 leaves comfrey
Large handful nettle tips
1 small onion sliced
1 medium potato peeled and sliced
7 fluid ozs. water

1 egg yolk
1 teaspoonful Marmite
Salt and pepper to taste
½ pint creamy milk
Whipped cream to garnish

Wash comfrey and nettle tips and remove middle rib from comfrey leaves and stalky bits from nettles. Put into a saucepan the comfrey, nettles, onion, potato, a little salt and the water. Cover with lid, simmer gently till everything is quite soft. Put through electric blender or fine sieve, add Marmite. Beat egg yolk and milk together and add to purée. It can then be heated or served cold.

Comfrey Soup

Make a white sauce with 1 oz. margarine, 1 oz. wholemeal flour and 1 pint of milk, add 3 to 4 tablespoonfuls of sieved comfrey (cooked first like spinach), 1 teaspoonful of Marmite or meat extract, salt and pepper and ½ pint of water. Bring to the boil and serve.

Comfrey Soufflé

Make a white sauce as above, cook until it leaves the sides of the saucepan, add 4 to 5 tablespoonfuls of sieved comfrey, beat in one after another the yolks of three eggs, and finally fold in the whites. Bake in a soufflé dish for 20 minutes. Recommended for poultry-keepers only.

Comfrey au Gratin

Wash and cook young comfrey leaves in boiling water to which 1 tablespoonful of salt has been added. Sieve or chop when cooked. Put a layer of cooked whole rice on the bottom of a fireproof dish, and a layer of comfrey, a dash of Yorkshire relish, sprinkle thickly with grated cheese and dot with a few dabs of margarine. Repeat till the dish is full, finishing with rice and cheese. Put some margarine on top, and fill it up with milk or milk and stock mixed. Bake in a fairly hot oven for about 30 minutes then serve.

Comfrey Green Drinks

These were invented by the late Dr. H. R. Kirschner in the U.S.A. as a way of taking allantoin through the summer. Take about four large leaves, plus a teacupful of cold water and put them through the electric liquidizer. Then pour through a sieve into a glass, and the result is a bright green fluid that can be drunk easily.

In the U.S.A. this type of drink is widely popular, as a method of taking allantoin for coughs and colds, and adding vitamin B12 to a vegan diet far more cheaply and easily than by taking comfrey tablets, which are expensive there. The evidence from backyard comfrey eaters is that liquidized comfrey does cure the sore tongue symptoms of B12 shortage, though in theory there is far too little to have any effect. This may well be because comfrey contains fewer indigestible analogues than the synthetic tablets, but it could also be the faith healing effect, which does not usually work for dietary deficiencies.

Bocking No. 14 is too bitter to make an attractive drink, which may be because of its higher potash, and when it is drunk raw it will be understood why rabbits dislike it. Bocking No. 4 or a Bocking Mixture is far pleasanter liquidized, and in the U.S. the last is regarded as a herb for making into summer drinks. Because it has not very much flavour it is usually blended with banana or other fruit, or even raw carrot. As the protein breaks down fast, liquidized comfrey is always made fresh. Mrs. Beth Setzer of Seattle invented a cocktail she calls 'Vodfrey' which is 75 per cent comfrey and 25 per cent vodka.

Comfrey Tea

There are many small scale methods of making comfrey tea: the most popular way is to stretch a length of expanded metal or inch mesh wire netting between four posts so that it is at least a foot off the ground and then spread the leaves thinly on the surface in the sun. This will wilt them flabby very quickly and they can then be transferred to an airing cupboard to crisp. Break it up by rubbing through a half inch sieve and packet in polythene bags to prevent its taking up moisture from the air, sealing them with sellotape.

The best flavour comes from the quickest drying, and snipping the midribs out hastens the process. If the midribless leaves are placed in boxes on a greenhouse shelf they dry easily and can be crisped off over a convector electric fire. If they go in an electric oven turned low, leave the door slightly open to let the steam out, but beware of overheating. Small scale drying is easy. It is when labour costs are considered that it ceases to be economic.

In 1965 Dr. A. H. Ward, analyst to the H.D.R.A., tested tea made by two different methods to determine the allantoin:

1. Allantoin content determined in the usual way after alcoholic extraction—0·083 per cent.
2. Two heaped teaspoonfuls (4 gm.) used to make four cupfuls (600 ml.) of tea, by pouring on the boiling water and steeping for 5 minutes. Amount of allantoin extracted—0·045 per cent.
3. 4 gm. of the sample boiled with 600 ml. of water for 5 minutes. Amount of allantoin extracted—0·046 per cent. There appears to be no significant difference in the proportion of allantoin extracted by the two tea-making procedures.

These were leaf-only samples, for the major portion of the allantoin is in stems and midribs, but it will be seen that the tea as drunk from both methods is approximately the same as the strength recommended for sores and gastric ulcers in the early editions of the British Pharmacopœia. It is usually made in Britain by putting two heaped teaspoonfuls of comfrey tea in a pot for two, plus two level ones of ordinary tea. Milk and sugar to taste.

Comfrey tea adds a certain 'smoothness' to ordinary tea and its flavour is not intrusive. Herbalists often recommend it with other teas and this is why it is so rare that a conclusive result is obtainable from a herbal treatment—so many ingredients are used at once that it is not possible to judge the one responsible for any effect.

Home dried comfrey can be ground to a green flour with a hand

wheat mill as used by home breadmakers or the grinder attach-
ment for a liquidizer, and commercially made flour can sometimes
be bought.

Fried Comfrey Flour for Vegans

Mix comfrey flour, soya flour and wholemeal flour in equal
quantities with sunflower seed oil, and fry, stirring for about 10
minutes in moderate heat. This can be kept in a jar for a week as a
nourishing and first-class protein as a base for gravies, soups and
stews. It can be added to the various nut savoury mixtures
available at the health stores to make rissoles, and to scramble eggs.
According to liking for comfrey, smaller or larger quantities can
be added.

Tomato is the best contrasting flavour to offset the comfrey. For
those who do not like comfrey, it can be disguised by adding curry
powder to the mixture.

Comfrey Flour Soup for Vegans

Take equal quantities of soya flour, 100 per cent compost-grown
wholemeal and comfrey flour, and very gently mix together in
vegetable oil (sunflower seed, peanut, corn oil) until a smooth
paste has formed. To this gradually add vegetable stock (water in
which vegetables have been cooked, plus Yeastrel or Marmite).
This is a superb mixture for building up health and for alleviating
under-nourishment and complaints of nervous origin, such as
asthma.

Comfrey Flour as a Winter Green Vegetable

Mash potatoes with milk and butter until they are very moist,
then just before serving, add the comfrey flour mixed in thoroughly.
Colour can be disguised by covering with raw grated carrots or
tomatoes. Several tablespoonfuls of the flour may be added, but
it is wiser to start with smaller amounts, as the raw flour may swell
up in the stomach and cause some discomfort if too large a
quantity is used. Comfrey flour can be added to most things, but is
best added just before serving as too hot liquids tend to make it

gluey and less palatable. It can be mixed with butter and various nut rissole mixtures for a tea sandwich.

All these preservation methods are expensive and cannot make a worthwhile contribution to world protein shortage. They are 'healthfoods' rather than 'wholefoods', because of their cost. What the world needs is a method of extracting the $3\frac{1}{2}$ tons a year of pure protein there is in a 100 ton an acre crop, compared with the 5 cwt. there is in a 15 cwt. an acre crop of soya beans. That is going to take a great deal more research than I have ever had the money to do, for it is not even analysis that is required, but engineers with the time and capital to experiment and develop processes from laboratory successes.

10. Comfrey in medicine

Research into the medicinal possibilities of comfrey suffers not only from the shortage of money—it is further handicapped by the absence of acceptable clinical data. Though I could fill perhaps four chapters with reported successes with comfrey as ointment, tea, tablets or fresh, none of this evidence would be accepted medically. It is mere anecdote to any doctor in every country, and because comfrey is to them folk medicine or herbalism, no research has been done.

For over twenty years I have been receiving letters from terminal cancer cases, and medically hopeless people, who have been told that orthodox medicine can do nothing more for them, except (in the U.S.A.) insist that they pay their bills. I am a gardener, not a doctor, and I am not going to risk having someone trust comfrey on my advice and die, when he or she might have been saved by surgery. I cannot know if the cases *are* hopeless still, and I cannot afford to risk the work that I have done in my own field, of cut and weighed yield figures, replicated plots, and analysis which are as well established as any other agricultural research, by writing of 'cures' I am not qualified to judge, which rest on hearsay, and on the enthusiasm of individuals who may well be justified.

All I can do is use the work of Dr. Charles MacAllister, who died in 1940, as the material for this chapter. It is true that he wrote in 1935 and much of his work was outdated by the discovery of M & B, and antibiotics, but he did it well, and he was qualified. His widow presented the copyright of the small, privately printed book he wrote on comfrey to the H.D.R.A. so that her husband's work should go on, and I use it here in the hope that some hospital or doctor somewhere will start some genuine research.

Through all the years I have lived with comfrey, I have offered leaf, ointment, tea, flour and plants free to any hospital or nature clinic prepared to work with comfrey. But I have had no takers. The unorthodox will not undertake research either. There has never been a comfrey clinic or 'comfrey cure' in any country, but I still hope that it will be possible for others to do the work for which I am not qualified.

What I can do is pass on the methods which have been used in comfrey treatments purely as recipes. All I say is that these treatments have helped a great many people.

Fresh Comfrey Leaf Tea

Boil six large leaves in two pints of water. Let it stand cooling for four hours after it has come to the boil, then strain the liquid into a 2 lb. jam jar and fit on a tight cover. It will keep for several days and tastes quite pleasant. Take half a teacupful night and morning.

Comfrey Flour Poultices

Equal parts of comfrey flour and starch. Mix the starch to a smooth paste with cold water. Add just sufficient boiling water to 'turn' the starch making a runny paste. Mix in the comfrey flour, allowing it to take up surplus water to make a smooth paste.

The consistency of this mixture is such that it may be moulded and applied direct to the part without the use of an intervening layer of material. It will lift on and off the skin easily and cleanly, and, if the technique is good, will retain the heat for some considerable time, provided sufficient of the constituents are used to allow the uptake of a considerable amount of boiling water, and that no time is lost in transit and in bandaging the preparation to the affected part.

Another way is to add to comfrey flour in a dish sufficient boiling water to make a stiff paste. Spread on lint or several layers of gauze. Cover top with a double layer of gauze. Apply to the part as hot as can be borne, the side with the double layer of gauze separating the poultice from the skin, so that the comfrey makes contact through it.

A heated metal dish should be used to prepare the poultice,

which should be carried to the patient between two heated metal plates. This is a precaution against infection, for though comfrey can inhibit bacterial growth, it is not a disinfectant.

Comfrey Tea (medicinal)

Where fresh leaf is not available in winter in temperate climates. Pour one quart of boiling water on 1 oz. of comfrey tea, and allow to stand for ten minutes before pouring through a tea strainer. This is taken both by mouth and as a retained enema, as an internal healer.

Comfrey Ointment

The H.D.R.A. has sold many thousands of tins of comfrey ointment made by pharmaceutical chemists, and there are many other makes all of which should be used as directed by the makers. No recipe is given for comfrey ointment because of the risk that the proteins will break down and undesirable bacteria get in. Making comfrey tea and poultices for immediate use with boiling water involves safe sterilization, but making an ointment and keeping it could mean a serious risk of infection especially when used with sores or open wounds.

Conclusion

There are thousands of people all over the world who have been helped by comfrey. It is possible that some of these people may be grateful enough to write out a clear and detailed account of their cases, if possible with the name and address of their doctor and permission for an H.D.R.A. doctor member to write to him to check exactly what happened in medical terms. I should very much like to hear from anyone with this kind of report so that I can pass it on to further medical research. Write c/o The Henry Doubleday Research Association, Bocking, Braintree, Essex.

THE MEDICINAL USES OF COMFREY
by Dr. Charles MacAlister, M.D., F.R.C.P.

About twenty-five years ago (1910–11), when endeavouring to make some investigations concerning cell proliferants, I happened to remember that in 1896 I had published a paper in the *Lancet* on 'Blood as a Therapeutic Agent', in which were incorporated some impressions which I had formed concerning bodies contained in blood which I thought might inhibit irregular cell growth. On looking up this paper I found in the same number of the *Lancet* an exceedingly interesting address entitled 'Some Surprises and Mistakes' by Professor William Thompson, President of the Royal College of Surgeons in Ireland. He recorded the case of a man who was suffering from a tumour involving the nose and antrum which, on being removed, was declared by Dr. O'Sullivan, Professor of Pathology in Trinity College, Dublin to be a round-celled sarcoma. The growth returned and the patient consulted Sir Felix Semon, on whose advice the jaw was removed and at the operation the tumour was found to occupy the whole of the antrum. The base of the skull was everywhere infiltrated by it. It had perforated the septum of the nose to which it was adherent, and had entered into the opposite (left) nostril. A month later the growth had again returned, it bulged through the incision and almost closed the right eye. It was blue, tense, firm and lobulated, but it did not break. Further operation being out of the question the man was sent to his home. About three months afterwards the patient walked into Professor Thompson's study looking in better health than he had ever seen him. The tumour had completely disappeared from the face and there was no trace of it in the mouth. He had no pain, and after having an obturator plate made to fill the opening which was left by the removal of the hard palate he went home apparently well. He told Professor Thompson that he had treated it by applying poultices of comfrey and the swelling had gradually disappeared. Professor Thompson said in his paper: 'I am as satisfied as can be that the growth was malignant and of bad type . . . I know nothing of the effects of comfrey root but

I do not believe that it could remove a sarcomatous tumour.'

There have been one or two cases in my own experience where undoubtedly malignant growths spontaneously disappeared, and the one which I have quoted may have been another example, but it set me thinking about the possibility that comfrey might contain some substance capable of controlling or stabilizing cell-growth, and it naturally led to an investigation of the literature of comfrey and to experiments being made with it clinically. At the time I had never heard of comfrey being used medicinally. It was certainly not included among the botanical agencies dealt with in classes of materia medica when I was a student, but it became evident from a reading of the old herbals that it was regarded as an important and valuable remedy in bygone days.

Historical

Comfrey belongs to the Boraginaceae or Borage-worts. It is referred to very casually in the books on Materia Medica, written after the middle of the nineteenth century. Pereira* (1854) says that formerly several Borage-worts were used in medicine and he mentions among them the *Symphytum officinale*, but he says 'they possess little medicinal value (though formerly many virtues were were ascribed to them), and are now obsolete.'

According to the Oxford English Dictionary the name Comfrey was of middle English origin and is attributed to the old French confirie or conflere, no doubt the equivalent of the modern confire —to preserve. It was also called Consolida, or, in some of the English Herbals, Consound, and was a member of a class of remedies referred to for instance in the Pharmacopoeia Londinensis Collegarum (1668) among the Radices or Roots as the Consolida or *Symphytum major*, and among the Herbs, Leaves and Seeds the Consolidae include, besides the comfrey, the *Consolida media* (the Bugula) and the *Consolida mimina* or daisy, also *Consolida Saracenia* or Solidago, a variety of comfrey having knobbed roots. This was called the true Saracens' Consound or Wound-wort because it was used by the Turks and Saracens for healing wounds. William Salmon in his English Herbal (1710,

* Pereira, *Elements of Materia Medica*, 1854.

page 213) classifies it among the agglutinatives or symphitica, 'which is the reason that "Comfrey" is called Symphytum because of its glewing quality.' In several Herbals it is spoken of as the chief vulnerary for the same reason. Comfrey is known to English botanists as the *Symphytum officinale*, and be it noted that the word Symphytum is derived from the Greek EUMOUTOV, 'a facultate glutandi', i.e. from its glueing properties. The Latins used the word Consolida for the same reason, from consolidare 'to solder, close or glew up' (Salmon). Hence the English equivalent Consound often used in the herbals.

When the comfrey became *Symphytum officinale* in England I am not sure. The term Officinal first came into use in its application to medicines, according to the Oxford Dictionary, in 1693; the Latin *Officina* being applied to the storeroom of a monastery in which medicines, etc., were kept, and so herbs, plants, drugs, etc., kept in stock in an apothecary's shop became 'Officinal' or as being of recognized utility. Comfrey was never introduced into the British Pharmacopoeia but it is described in Squire's *Companion to the British Pharmacopoeia* (17th edition, page 619) as having astringent, mucilaginous and glutinous properties. Its author knew a bone-setter who had rendered himself famous by treating fractures with a pulp made of the scraped root spread to the thickness of a crown piece upon cambric or old muslin which was wrapped round the limb and bandaged over. It soon stiffened, giving great strength and support to the part, and the bandage was not removed until the limb was well.

Squire mentions that comfrey was officially recognized in the following Pharmacopœias: in Belgium as *Radix symphyti*; France *Consonde*; Mexico *Sinfito*; Portugal *Consolida major*; Spain *Sinfito major*; and in no others.

There are three varieties of comfrey referred to in the herbals: (1) the *Symphitum majus vulgare* or Common Great Comfrey: (2) the *Symphitum majus flore purpureo*—the Great Comfrey with purple flowers; (3) the *Symphitum tuberosum* or Comfrey with knobbed roots, which is the Saracen Consound formerly mentioned. This latter has several species and was probably selected on account of the largeness of its roots. All the varieties were used, however, the roots being gathered during the winter months (October to March). The leaves, also employed, were gathered in June and July during and after inflorescence.

The medical chronology of the plant is interesting no account of its antiquity. In the *New English Dictionary*, Saxon Leechdom is quoted (*c.* 1000) 'This Wort strengthens the man,' and it states, 'Ad fluxum Sanguinis accipe de Confirma, hoc est consolida.' In the Saxon Herbarium it was thus recommended for one 'Bursten Within'; the leaves were roasted in hot ashes and mixed with honey and then taken fasting. There are many references to comfrey, and I cannot do better than quote some details of its history from a paper by the late Professor R. J. Harvey Gibson* which gives a very good historical summary. He says 'In Sarracenius's version of Dioscorides, published in 1596, descriptions are given of two species of *Symphytum*: Chap. IX (Liber 11) is headed "De symphytopetraeo" and Chap. X "De Symphyto Altero." The "roots" and their "vertues" are described in the following terms: "Radices demit-tunter foris nigrae, intus candidae, glutinosae, quarumetiam est usus. Tritae et potae sanguinem excreantibus ruptisque proficiunt et recentia vulnera imposite glutinant; carnum quoque frustra quibuscum conjungunter cogunt ita ut coalescant. Caeterum inflammationibus, prae sertimque sedis, cum Senecionis foliis utiliter illinunter".'

Bock, in his work, *De stirpium* (Kyber's edition, 1552), quotes and expands this sentence from Dioscorides, and describes the then recognized methods of application of the plant, internally and externally. Fuchs also (1542) quotes the same extract, and also the views of Galen and Pliny, which are practically in the phraseology of Dioscorides.

In W. Turner's *Herball* (1568) the following occurs: 'Of Comfrey Symphytum. The rootes are good if they be broken and dronken from them that spitte blood, and are bursten. The same, layd to, are good to glewe together freshe woundes. They are also good to be layd to inflammation, and specially of the fundament,

---

* Note on the Anatomy History of *Symphytum officinale* by R. J. Harvey Gibson, M.A., F.Z.S., Prof. of Botany, University of Liverpool, *Pharmaceutical Journ. and Pharmacist*, 27 January, 1912.

with the leaves of groundsell'. This account is also merely a condensed translation of Dioscorides.

Dodoens, in his *Cruydtboeck*, translated by Lyte (1578), expands Turner's statement, adding that when 'mengled with sugar, syropes, or honny . . . are good to be layde upon all hoate tumours.' Quite similar statements as to the value of comfrey rhizome are made in Bulleyn's *Herbal* (1562) and in the *Adversaria* of Pena and Lobelius (1570), and the *Stirpium Historia* of the latter author (1576), also in the spitome of Camerius (1586). J. Bauhin (*Historia*, 1651) expresses his concurrence in the views of the sixteenth century herbalists as to the curative value of decoctions of comfrey in all cases of wounds, blood-spitting, or even broken limbs.

Gerard's *Herbal* (1597) repeats, but at somewhat greater length, the same account. He asserts the efficacy of comfrey also in healing up 'ulcers of the lunges' and 'ulcers of the kidneies, though they have been of long continuance.' Parkinson (*Theatrum Botanicum*, 1640) gives the same general description of the 'vertues' of comfrey, but adds: 'The roots of Comfrey, taken fresh, beaten small, spread upon leather, and laid upon any place troubled with the gout, doe presently give ease of the paines: and applyed in the same manner giveth ease to paid joynts, and profiteth very much for running and moist ulcers, gangrenes, mortifications, and the like.' There is a marble statue of John Parkinson (born 1567), Apothecary to King James I, outside the Palm House, Sefton Park, Liverpool.

In the *Compleat Herbal* of Tournefort (1719) a long account is given of the 'vertues' of comfrey and of its general characters. It is interesting that this author states that 'upon a chymical analysis the Comfrey yields many acid liquids, much earth, very little sulphur and no concreted volatile salt but a small quantity of a urinous spirit and a very moderate quantity of fixed salts.' Tournefort closes his account with the observations of Hierobymus Rensuerus 'that a charlatan cured a certain person of a malignant ulcer, pronounced to be a cancer, by the surgeons, and left by them as incurable, by applying twice a day the root of Comfrey bruised, having first peeled off the external blackish bark or rind; but the cancer was not above eight or ten weeks standing.'

By the end of the eighteenth century comfrey seems to have declined in popularity among physicians; thus Woodville (*Medical Botany*, 1794) writes: 'A supposed vulnerary efficacy, for which this plant was formerly in great repute, and to which it seems to owe its name' (comfrey ... confirma), 'will now be considered as nothing in its recommendation.' He adds: 'the mucilaginous matter is the only medicinal principle, and may be used as an emollient and demulcent.'

There are many other references to comfrey which all tell the same story, and it is unnecessary to elaborate the evidence that it was at one time held in high repute by the medical profession. An interesting point is the fact that in country districts it is still valued by agricultural and other workers on account of its curative properties. When visiting a farm at Tarvin in Cheshire many years ago, I was interested to find that its owner always kept a bed of comfrey in order that he might provide villagers with it when occasions arose. Dr. Walter Moore, of Bourton-on-the-Water, has recently informed me that, within his recollection, plots of it were grown as a food for cattle, on account of its reputation for producing milk, rich both in quality and quantity. Another interesting Gloucestershire reference is contained in a letter published by Mr. Edwin Green of Cheltenham* in 1912 in which he wrote that in Gloucestershire this plant when cooked in the same way as spinach is used very largely by many people during the spring. He stated that it is well known there as a blood purifier not only for human beings but also for cattle and horses, the effect on the latter being to produce a wonderful glossy coat. He knew a gentleman near Cheltenham who had a field of four acres in which nothing but this plant was grown. He gave it not only to his horses but was never without a dish of it, when in season, instead of spinach.

One more point before leaving the history of this interesting plant. Dr. Edward Nicholson, of Neuilly (Seine), who furnished numerous references when I was first working on this subject, stated in one of his letters (15 November, 1911): 'I am quite at one with you in the examination of forgotten "Worts". Certainly until

* *Daily Mail*, 27 March, 1912.

the manufacture of the new class of synthetic medicines prevailed, one could count on one's fingers medicines that had not been discovered by old women or savages, and now one finds that some of these synthetic remedies are scientific imitations (however unconsciously) of the "principles" contained in the old Herbals.'

No doubt in the past, as in the present, the introduction of new methods of treatment led to the disuse of old ones. Fashions in medicines changed then as now, and many really valuable natural remedies belonging to the periods of rational empiricism were left behind and forgotten or relegated to the limbo of lost reputations.

I myself have heard comfrey spoken of as an 'old woman's remedy,' and I admit it in the sense that it probably dates from the time when woman was the Priestess of Medicine. I referred to this in a paper on 'The Psychology of Nursing,' written for the *Cripples Journal* in 1928, in which I stated that Nursing is a profession which pre-eminently belongs to woman, and the psychology of the nurse is essentially that of woman, who throughout the ages has been regarded as the possessor of inborn gifts and attributes which render her the natural tender of the weak and sick and of the maimed and hurt . . . this is related to the maternal instincts which are present, although they may be dormant in a greater or lesser degree, in every woman; instincts concerned but not only with the propagation of the race but with its preservation. The experiences which woman acquired in prehistoric times regarding the care of her offspring during childhood and beyond was probably associated with the same knowledge which would be handed on from mother to daughter. So it would happen that adults appealed to woman as to a mother when smitten with illness. She was the witch or wise woman of those days—and it is within the realms of possibility that comfrey was among the 'simples' employed by her, and may truly be called an old or ancient 'woman's remedy'.

Some idea of the traditional therapeutic virtues of comfrey may be gathered from the names by which it was popularly known. For instance Knitbacke (Gerrard 1597), Comfort Knitbene (Scotland) in Aberdeen it was called Comfer Knitbeen, and a preparation made by boiling the root in oil or lard was extolled by old women for hardening and strengthening fractures. This property also accounted for its being called Bone-set or Knit Bone in Lancashire. It appears to have been used both internally and externally in fractures in all districts.

A rather amusing letter received from a doctor in Lancashire in 1912 illustrates the faith of the people in Comfrey as a healer. He wrote: 'Three years ago I was called to see a girl with gastric ulcer, haematemesis and severe vomiting and treated the case in the usual orthodox manner. In three weeks the patient was able to return to the mill. When congratulating the mother on her daughter's speedy recovery the old woman said to me:

"Do you mind my telling you something Doctor?" On my replying in the negative—

"Well" she said, "my girl has never had a drop of your medicine and all she has supped is pints of strong Comfrey tea."

'Since this occasion I have found it an excellent sedative for the gastric mucous membrane.'

Clinical Observations with Comfrey

Having become acquainted with the history of the plant and kinds of maladies for the treatment of which preparations made from it have been employed, the next procedure was to try it out and discover whether it possessed any of the therapeutic properties ascribed to it. Professor Harvey Gibson had obtained a large quantity of the ground and unground rhizome, some of which was handed to Dr. Titherley, then head of the Organic Chemistry Department, University of Liverpool, and Mr. Norman Coppin, who was working in the laboratory of Professor Benjamin Moore (Biochemistry), and while they were making a careful chemical investigation of it, which took a considerable time, I proceeded to dress the only ulcer which was then available with a strong infusion made from the powdered root.

This case was an exceedingly unpromising one because it was a 'rodent' of about two years' duration, not a simple ulcer.

The patient was a woman aged 87, and it seemed a suitable case for observation following the history of the malignant growth recorded by Professor Thompson which originated this research.

It was a stroke of fortune that this case was the first one to be experimented upon because, having resisted all kinds of previous treatment, the marked epithelial growth which took place upon it seemed more likely to be the result of a specific action of the application than would have been the case in an ordinary varicose ulcer for instance.

It was a very large ulcer (measuring 4 by 3 inches) involving the skin and deeper structures over the upper thorax and it was slowly spreading, more especially by its upper margin which was high and undermined; the other margins were less raised. The base was irregular and there was some seropurulent discharge. After being dressed with the mucilaginous infusion for about a week the surface cleaned and a distinct ingrowth of epithelium could be seen taking place from some of the marginal points. Later on the upper margin flattened somewhat on its inner aspect, the under-mining vanished, and after growing here and breaking down there for a time the epithelium became stronger and closed in to a considerable extent.

By this time Dr. Titherley reported to me that he had obtained a definite, so-far unidentified, crystalline body from the root and he was able to give me sufficient of this to experiment with. Since it was very sparingly soluble in water, quite a large amount of solution was made which was now used as a dressing for the ulcer instead of the infusion. With this application the skinning over process took place more rapidly and in the course of a month was all but completed. Unfortunately the taking of a photograph was put off in the hope of getting a picture of the completely covered ulcer.

It was never obtained however because through the perverse-ness of fortune the aged patient contracted influenza, which was epidemic in the institution at the time and she died of bronchitis. As a matter of fact this was the only ulcer initially treated with the infusion of comfrey root alone, and the fact that epithelial growth was further hastened after dressing it with a solution of the crystalline body suggested that this might be the active principle which promoted healing.

That infusions of the root are very active, however, was indicated by descriptions of cases treated with it which came from a variety of sources. One of the most striking was published in the *British Medical Journal* of 8 June, 1912, by Dr. Charles Searle of Cambridge. The case had the following history:

The patient was a man aged 83, first seen on 23 October, 1911. He suffered from shortness of breath, and swelling of the legs on which were some ulcers due to neglect. For some months this condition was very grave; he had marked arteriosclerosis, a loud aortic systolic murmur, with a feeble pulse and low temperature. The urine contained blood, albumen, and casts, but no sugar.

During December 1911, a fungating ulcer appeared on the dorsum of the left foot. It rapidly spread, and eventually exposed the metatarsal bones. In January 1912, the patient's condition appeared to be hopeless, he became at times delirious, and was removed home to die. He was then treated with four-hourly fomentations made with decoction of comfrey root. The ulcer immediately began to fill up rapidly and was practically healed by the end of April, and the patient's condition made corresponding improvement.

Several medical men were kind enough to confirm my observations from their own experiences with infusions of comfrey for the treatment of ulcers, but further reference to this must be deferred until I come to speak of allantoin which proved to be the actual crystalline body extracted from the root.

I must state at this point that neither comfrey nor its constituent is a specific for rodent ulcers. The case of rodent ulcer recorded which raised considerable hopes, naturally led to others being similarly dealt with, but without convincing results.

The Chemical Research

Before proceeding to describe the clinical and other observations which led to the conclusion that allantoin has to do with cell growth, it may be as well to give a short account of the result of the analysis whereby this substance was isolated from Comfrey and of some of its chemical characteristics. In his preliminary examination Dr. Titherley established the facts that the root contained:

(1) Gums
(2) Sugars, including a reducing sugar
(3) Resins
(4) A protocatechuic derivative or derivatives
(5) A substance giving an intense yellow solution with sodium hydrate (not investigated further)
(6) A crystalline solid, which was isolated in a pure condition.

It was very rich in nitrogen and melted at 226°C. Since from clinical observations this latter body appeared to be the physiologically active constituent of the root, Mr. Coppin was asked to devote his attention to its investigation. Ultimately Dr. Titherley and he found that the root contained about 0·8 per cent of this crystalline substance, and by accurate determination of its carbon, hydrogen, and nitrogen contents, showed that it possessed the same empirical formula as allantoin, which it greatly resembled in its chemical properties.

Allantoin

Some allantoin was now prepared from uric acid, and the product from the root was proved conclusively to be an identical substance by chemical methods. For example, allantoic acid and other derivatives were prepared both from the chemically made allantoin and from that obtained from the root; their melting points were the same, and so forth.

Allantoin ($C_4H_6N_4O_3$) is a compound which is obtained by the alkaline oxidation of uric acid in the cold.

Uric Acid   *Allantoin*

It is a white crystalline substance, melting at about 226°C., with decomposition. It is only slightly soluble in cold water (0·6 per cent), but readily in hot water. It is rather more soluble in cold alcohol, but it is quite insoluble in ether. Dry allantoin is quite

stable, but if boiled with water for a considerable time it undoubtedly undergoes decomposition to some extent. It is decomposed by alkali, giving a variety of products, the nature of
which entirely depend upon the conditions under which the
experiment is carried out. It will be seen from Dr. Titherley's
description of the chemical constitution of allantoin (p. 240) that
he gives it two distinct chemical formulae: one a single five-atom
ring (mono-cyclic) with ureide side chain, the other a double (bi-
cyclic) five-atom ring constitution without side chain, and he
shows that one form passes into the other by the mere wandering
of a hydrogen atom.

Quoting his words from a letter 3 May, 1933, descriptive of these
peculiarities he says: 'One of these forms (the double cyclic) I call
pseudo-allantoin, and I think, though it has never been proved,
that it is soluble in water. At all events in one of the synthetic
experiments I got a soluble form which on standing passes over
into the ordinary familiar crystals. This soluble form is too unstable to keep. I mention these facts to illustrate what I mean by
saying that allantoin is a peculiar substance, and I believe that
Nature somehow utilizes those peculiarities in cell metabolism'.

It may be well at this point to refer to the fact that when carrying
out some experiments concerning the action of allantoin on
leucocytes during two periods separated by an interval of several
years, I got such a diversity of results that I wrote to Dr. Titherley
in 1933 suggesting a possible instability in the allantoin crystals
which might be brought about by gradual decomposition. I was
led to suspect this because the diversity disappeared on using
freshly prepared crystals. In his reply Dr. Titherley referred to the
tautomeric properties of the substance, and its peculiarity in
undergoing the changes in chemical constitution, above referred
to, probably due to this tautomerism. He did not think it should
alter its therapeutic behaviour, however, since an equilibrium
would be set up between the two forms in solution, but he considered it conceivable that this equilibrium is only slowly obtained
by pure water, and perhaps more quickly if a trace of alkali or acid
is present. He knew nothing on this point about allantoin, but it
certainly occurs in other organic tautomeric compounds where the

rate of attainment in equilibrium solution is enormously dependent on traces of other substances which accelerate the change by
catalysis.

This is more or less by the way, but it has been thought well to
mention it as pointing to the necessity for dissolving the crystals in
distilled water. This precaution was observed in the first (original)
set of experiments, but in the later one which gave such different
results tap water was almost certainly used by an independent
observer.

The Chemical Physiology of Allantoin

Regarding the chemical physiology of allantoin, or the part which
it plays in human metabolism, very little is known, but some
interesting facts have been recorded which may throw light upon
its action as a cell-proliferant, and may point to its having a
function to perform in the bodily chemistry apart from any
possibility of its being a product of purine metabolism, in which
light it has generally been regarded. It is present both in animals
and in plants. It was first discovered in the former, and received
its name from the fact that it was found in the foetal allantoic
fluid. Later on it was identified in the urine of pregnant women.
Its presence has been demonstrated in very small amounts as a
normal constituent of the urines of healthy people; but that it is
not an end-product of human metabolism—which means that it is
probably not derived from the oxidation of uric acid, to which it
is closely allied—has been shown by a good many observers, as
pointed out by Dr. Ackroyd in a paper published in the *Biochemical Journal* for March 1911. This is an important observation, and is based upon the work of Schittenhelm, Wiener,
Minkowski, Poduschka, and Wiechowski, who have shown that
when allantoin is given to man it can be recovered to a considerable extent in the urine; and the author himself concludes 'that
the whole quantity of allantoin excreted by man on a milk and
vegetable diet may be derived directly from that contained in the
food'. You will note that I am speaking of the relation of allantoin
to human metabolism only. In the dog, cat and rabbit it appears to
be a normal end-product of metabolism, and experiments made

upon them seem to show that the giving of foods rich in purines, such as thymus and pancreas, gives rise in the two former animals to increased allantoin elimination; and in the latter animal the addition of sodium nucleate alone and sodium nucleate together with uric acid to the fodder, resulted in almost all the purine products being excreted in the allantoic fraction of the urine.* Furthermore, the same observer noted that the intravenous injection of nucleic acid caused an increase only in purine bases and allantoin, and that the ingestion of allantoin itself caused in these animals a marked increase in the total nitrogen that was ingested. The difference between the metabolism of these animals and that of man is well shown by Wiechowski, who found that, given subcutaneously, uric acid appears mostly as allantoin in the urines of the dog and rabbit, whereas in human urine about 90 per cent is excreted unaltered.†

If these facts are reliable, the allantoin in human urine is mainly derived from vegetable foods and from milk, which Dr. Ackroyd found to contain about 0·019 grm. per litre, and in the healthy individual it appears to pass practically unchanged through the economy, the amount eliminated representing the amount which had been ingested.

In this relation, however, its tautomeric qualities and the influences of catalysis already referred to should be remembered.

Distribution of Allantoin in the Vegetable Kingdom

Our knowledge of this is not very extensive but it is a very suggestive fact that such analyses as have been made indicate that it is generally found in parts which are related to growth, either active or potential. We have a striking example of this in the Comfrey where it is present in the roots and terminal buds. The leaves have not yet been thoroughly investigated, but the interesting point is the large amount of allantoin in the rhizome, greater than in any plants heretofore investigated. E. Schulze and J. Barbieri‡ in 1881–82 found it in the buds of certain plants and in the bark of

* Schittenhelm and Seisser, *Zeitschr. Expt. Path. Ther.*, 1909, vii, 116–133.
† Wiechowski, *Biochem. Zeitschr.*, 1910, xxv, 431–459.
‡ *Journ. of Prak. Chem.* (2) xxv, 147.

branches of trees and Ackroyd refers to its identification by Richard Crampton (1886) in the embryos of wheat separated in the process of milling and in beet juice. Ackroyd* himself demonstrated its presence in bread, french beans and green peas, whereas it is absent in bananas and rhubarb. This regional location of allantoin in plants is interesting when regarded in conjunction with the fact that it is a characteristic component of the foetal allantoic secretion, and related therefore to an important structure connected with the foetal circulation, a structure along which the vessels pass which convey the foetal blood to and from its intimate relationship with the maternal blood.

Whenever we find any substances constantly in certain parts of plants or animals, it is quite reasonable to suppose that they may be in some way related to and necessary for the particular tissues which have selected them; and although the allantoin in the human embryo might be regarded as a foetal waste product, I think we may feel justified in assuming that, in the economics of Nature, it has a function to perform, perhaps in relation to cell-multiplication, especially as it is not at once eliminated through the maternal circulation, and the same suggestion comes from the fact that it is also present in milk, the food of the rapidly growing young organism, and in those parts of some plants in which active cell-multiplication takes place.

Bearing on this comes a very interesting analogy between the presence of allantoin in the foetal allantois and in the root of the comfrey plant. In the earliest months of pregnancy, dating from the third week onwards, the allantois becomes relatively large, and the amount of allantoin contained in it corresponds to some extent to the size of the sack. The vessels of the chorion conveying the maternal blood to the foetus pass through the allantois and probably derive the allantoin from it to be utilized in the metabolism connected with growth and development. As pregnancy advances the allantois diminishes in size and length, shortly before the child is born, it becomes vestigial and the amount of allantoin infinitesimal. Compare this with the comfrey rhizome which in the earliest months of the year (January to March)

* *Biochem. Journ.,* v, 403.

contains from 0·6 to 0·8 per cent of allantoin. Analysed a couple of months later it contains about 0·4 per cent. In July the amount is still further diminished and when the plant is in full growth practically none is to be found in the rhizome but it is discoverable in the terminal buds, leaves, and young shoots. This important fact may be regarded as evidence that the plant withdraws allantoin from its storehouse in the rhizome and utilizes it for purposes of cell-proliferation. In continuation of the analogy above referred to it is interesting that the maternal milk contains about 0·006 per cent of allantoin, a fact that may have something to do with the further growth of the child after birth.

Experiments with Plants

The presence of allantoin in the underground reserves and growing parts of plants, as well as its relation to the foetus in the allantois and in milk—the food of the rapidly growing infant—added to the clinical evidence that it promotes healing in ulcerative conditions which will be referred to later, naturally led to the suggestion that experiments made upon plants might afford some information, confirmatory or otherwise, of its proliferative properties or functions. By my request Mr. Coppin planted a large number of hyacinth bulbs (the growth of which had been started in the dark) in solutions of allantoin varying from 0·1 to 0·5 per cent, and it was found that the growth of the roots was inhibited in a ratio proportionate to the amount of allantoin in the solution—that is, the stronger the solution the less was the amount of growth in the root.

Notwithstanding this diminished root growth, which was confirmed by microscopic examination, the flower stems of the plants grew in a stunted way, but none had blossomed at the end of twelve weeks, and it therefore appeared that allantoin did not promote cell-growth when added to the water in which the bulbs were growing, in fact their growth appeared to be retarded. This was disappointing, but an interesting development now ensued. It seemed certain that in plants the allantoin or other proliferant agent is stored for use in the rhizomes, buds, barks and germinal parts, and is probably elaborated there as the result of some metabolic process. There is no allantoin normally in the water or earth in which bulbs are grown, but it or some kindred substance is evidently formed and stored in the bulb or, in the case of other plants, in the rhizomes or roots, to be drawn upon as required for advancing the process of growth and development. This being the case, the suggestion naturally arose that one might try the effect of injecting a solution of allantoin into the bulbs, and a number of experiments were conducted on these lines, the first of which was made in a more or less casual way as follows:

A child in the Liverpool Royal Southern Hospital had two earth-grown hyacinths in a pot. They had grown quite unequally, one having developed well with the commencement of a flower, the other being feeble, short and showing no signs of blossom.

About 15 minims of allantoin solution (0·4 per cent) were injected on several occasions into the bulb of the latter, with the result that rapid growth ensued and it overgrew its more vigorous neighbour and flowered before it.

This experiment excited the interest of the Sister of the ward (Miss Archer) and of the Matron (Miss Jolly), and they gave similar injections into the bulbs of a considerable number of plants in about equal stages of growth. Controls were used, some being injected with quantities of water equal in amount to the quantities of allantoin solution given, others being grown without any injections; these experiments were conducted in earth-grown bulbs. In addition, some hyacinth bulbs which had just started growth, the shoots being about $\frac{1}{4}$ in. high, were planted in water, and some of them were injected every third or fourth day with allantoin solution, some with water only, the remainder being controls, and the same results were obtained in every case. The allantoin evidently acted as a cell-proliferant, forcing the growth of the shoots, and especially of the flowers (for it was noticeable that the plant often blossomed with comparatively little leaf growth), commonly before their untreated neighbours had reached anything like the stage of flower production. The water-injected plants grew better than the uninjected ones, but nothing like so rapidly as those to which allantoin had been added.

These experiments were repeated many times with tulips, lilies of the valley and other plants, care being taken to ensure that they were planted at the same time, in the same tubful of earth and under the same conditions of temperature and surroundings. These results have been confirmed many times, and in the cases of non-bulbous plants the injection of allantoin solution into or below the flower-buds or into the bases of individual spikes has resulted in the production of large flowers contrasting strongly with other untreated flowers or spikes on the same plant.

In the water-grown plants which were injected it was noted that with the increased growth of the shoots there was sometimes a diminished growth of the roots, which were considerably longer and stronger in the controls.

This led to the impression that perhaps the roots were not so necessary to the plant if its water as well as the proliferant content were kept high, and in order to test this point a number of hyacinth bulbs were selected which had shoots $\frac{1}{4}$ in. high but no visible roots. Some of these were injected with allantoin solution, some with water, others being uninjected, and they were simply placed upon a plate without earth or water. At the end of seven or eight days the little shoots of the treated plants were opening out into leaves. The water-injected bulbs also lived but did not grow so well, whereas the shoots of the controls browned at the tips and shrivelled up. Not a sign of roots made their appearance in any of these plants.

From these experiments one gathers the impression that allantoin is a substance which is capable of being utilized by vegetable cells in connection with their proliferative processes, just as there seems to be proof that it has proliferative properties in connection with certain animal cells, if one may judge by the way in which it promotes healing in chronic and acute ulcerative conditions which will be referred to later on. In both cases the reproduced cells are normal microscopically and resemble those from which they took their origin.

In connection with the injection of bulbs a medical man wrote to me many years ago explaining that in repeating my experiments his results were contradictory to those which I had obtained. His plants became stunted and growth was interfered with. On asking for details concerning his experiment it transpired that he had injected his bulbs with an infusion of comfrey which he had prepared by prolonged boiling of the roots. It is quite probable that the contained allantoin would be decomposed by the boiling, but there is also a possibility that in the root there may be a controlling substance uninfluenced by heat which retards growth. A research concerning this possibility was not proceeded with.

Clinical Observations

The original clinical observations made with allantoin were chiefly conducted in cases of superficial ulcers of various kinds, in order that the effects on the growth of epithelium might be carefully watched. In the selection of cases, great care was exercised in order to make certain that other conditions which would ordinarily promote healing were not alone operating and bringing about or starting cell-proliferation. On this account an endeavour was made to safeguard observations in the first place by dealing only with those ulcers which had refused to heal under ordinary conditions of rest and cleanliness, together with other forms of treatment, and in the second place a good many medical men were provided with fresh solutions of allantoin wherewith to treat their cases in order that our own results might be confirmed or tempered by theirs. One is rather apt, when experimenting with a substance in this way, to allow optimism to exaggerate the resultant benefits, and it is an advantage to get others to form independent judgements concerning them from their own observations.

After publishing some of these results, numerous applications for supplies of allantoin came from medical men, not only in this country but also from Canada and other Dominions, wherewith to treat cases under their immediate care, and many of them were good enough to record their results, some of which, being of great interest, will be referred to.

I was very fortunate in having surgical colleagues who were interested in this research, and numerous cases were placed at my disposal in the wards of the hospitals.

A striking case was that of a woman, aged 48, who was transferred to me by Mr. Douglas Crawford on 20 July, 1911. There was a large ulcer on the dorsum of the foot and another, practically continuous with it, over the lower third of the leg. The bases were in places sloughy and even gangrenous looking, and there was a purulent discharge. She was sent to Mr. Crawford, I understand, for his opinion as to whether the leg should be amputated. The ulcer measured 5 by 4 in., and had been in existence for five years. Allantoin dressings were commenced on 25 July. A week later the surface had cleaned and presented healthy granulations, and a rapid growth of epithelium was taking place from all the margins. On 12 August it was manifestly healing, and on 17 August, i.e. in twenty-three days, this huge ulcer was reduced to the size of a pin's head. The scar was healthy and sound. The patient was kept in bed for a fortnight, and after her discharge it remained sound and well.

Another class of ulcer which quickly responded to allantoin includes those which are apt to occur in paralytic cases. We had an example of this in a girl, aged 11 years, who had a large ulcer on the dorsum of her left foot. The skin had broken down rapidly, leaving a deep circular ulcer about the size of a penny.

Since it showed no signs of healing at the end of five weeks the late Sir Robert Jones invited me to dress it with allantoin. This treatment commenced on 10 March, 1911. The epithelium rapidly grew in, and in four weeks it was entirely healed.

Another case referred by Sir Robert Jones was that of a young woman who had circular paralytic ulcers on each leg. These were examples of what used to be called weak ulcers in my student days, and they had remained practically unchanged, one of them for five months and the other for eight months, in spite of the fact that the patient had been recumbent for several weeks. On 2 May they were dressed with allantoin; on the 17th the ulcer on the right leg was skinned over and those on the left leg healed soon afterwards. The epithelial coverings in this case were thin, and the cicatrices soft and flat. She was one of those patients with flail legs, the surface cold and muscles atonic, and one was not surprised to hear that one of the ulcers subsequently recurred.

I might quote many cases of various kinds which clearly confirmed the cell-proliferative qualities of allantoin. Among these were several cases of varicose ulcers, but it was found that burns and scalds of the lesser degrees were very useful fields for observation. This was because islets of epithelium, many of them at first invisible to the naked eye, formed centres from which new epithelial growths could be seen spreading from day to day with remarkable rapidity. In a letter to the *British Medical Journal* (13 January, 1912) Mr. R. W. Murray (Hon. Surgeon Liverpool Northern Hospital) confirmed the value of allantoin as a cell-proliferant as follows: "I can confirm Dr. MacAlister's remarks upon the value of allantoin as a cell proliferant. Towards the end of last year there was an explosion at works in the neighbourhood of the hospital and we were called upon to treat a large number of men who were severely burnt on the hands, forearms, and face. The burns were mostly of the second or third degree, and for about a week they were dressed with gauze soaked either in a solution of picric acid or in a solution of iodine.

'Dr. MacAlister asked me to try dressing them with allantoin, and kindly provided us with a quantity of it. In the first instance it was tried on two or three cases only, but the results were so satisfactory and so convincing to house-surgeons, dressers and nurses, that dressing with allantoin solution soon became general. It not only stimulates epithelial growth, but "cleans up" sloughing surfaces in a most remarkable fashion. When nurses and house-surgeons are really keen about any particular line of treatment there is generally something in it. This has certainly been our experience with allantoin.'

Mr. Murray's statement that allantoin cleans up sloughing surfaces applies not only to burns but to ulcers generally, and the question arose as to whether it possessed any antiseptic properties. This cleaning-up process is of course essential if healing is to occur, because healthy cell-proliferation will not take place over septic surfaces, and it was essential to determine whether the allantoin was primarily destructive to micro-organisms or promoted this effect by establishing physiological conditions in the cells and their surroundings which rendered them immune to micro-organisms. Some simple experiments had previously demonstrated that, far from being a poisonous antiseptic, it possesses no toxic qualities, and rather favours than inhibits culture growths of organisms. In August 1911, during a cruise to the Shetlands in the late Professor Sir William Herdman's yacht the *Runa*, I was able to make a number of observations concerning the effects which followed the placing of samples of the plankton gatherings (which were constantly available during tow-netting operations) in sea-water containing varying amounts of allantoin. The object of this was to discover whether the allantoin was destructive to the small and simple forms of animal and vegetable life which are found in the plankton. Owing to the active ways in which they move about, the most easily observed creatures were the copepoda, but there were many other forms which could easily be watched with the naked eye. An excess of allantoin was placed in a quantity of sea-water and thoroughly shaken up, so as to make as saturated a solution as possible, and of this quantities were added to newly drawn sea-water in proportions varying from 1·8, 1·7, and so forth up to saturated strength, controls of pure sea-water being employed in every series of experiments. The net result of a considerable number of observations was that the animalculae observed lived for nearly as long a time (about two days) in the saturated and other solutions as they did in the controls, and from this it appeared that allantoin was not appreciably inimical to the forms of life which were experimented upon.

On my return to Liverpool Dr. Alfred Adams, working in the Biochemical Laboratories of the University, made some experiments with various culture media, containing 0·2 per cent of allantoin, and on 1 November, 1911, he reported that the *Bacillus coli*, Staphylococci, Streptococci and Tubercle Bacilli were not retarded in their growth and multiplication by it.

Allantoin, then, is not an antiseptic in the usual acceptation of the term, and its action in this respect must depend upon some influence brought to bear upon the cells, whereby their resistance, stability and immunity are established and their proliferation promoted.

It has been explained that sundry independent workers had reported their experiences, and before going further one or two of these may be mentioned.

In February 1912, Dr. Mackenzie of Montreal was supplied with allantoin wherewith to treat a case of senile gangrene in the heel of an aged colleague who had been glycosuric for some years and had sclerosed vessels. He had been in bed for five weeks suffering much pain and the slough had not separated. The necrosed area was described as being over an inch in diameter and from half to three-quarters of an inch deep, this measurement being due to infiltration of the surrounding tissues. The necrosis extended down to the os calcis; it was not thought, however, that the periosteum had been denuded. The allantoin was at once applied on its arrival in 0·5 per cent solution, and immediately promoted cleaning up, separation of the slough and much relief from pain. The report stated that there was a continuous improvement after the new dressing was employed, and the cavity ultimately closed with a stellate scar.

The late Dr. Arthur Wallace (Surgeon to the Liverpool Women's Hospital), reported the closure of an intractable biliary fistula following operation for gall-stones. Ten days after the first dressing with allantoin solution, applied by means of a gauze wick, bile ceased to escape and the sinus steadily healed. He reported another case of local necrosis following a pressure sore and others in which drainage tube tracks had been slow in healing which were greatly benefited by treatment on similar lines.

An ophthalmic surgeon employed allantoin dressings for a patient having a very extensive and deep burn of the eyeball and lids, due to molten copper, and expressed himself astonished at the result. He wrote: 'The disappearance of the chemosis, the firm healing of the deeper layers and the formation of new tissue have been most marked and have even astonished the nurses who know nothing about the stuff.'

There were many other writers on the subject but it would only labour the point to refer to their comments and expressions concerning the effects produced in the way of cell-proliferation.

Just a few words may be permitted concerning the use of allantoin in internal ulcerative conditions where no ocular demonstrations of the healing process have been possible. Comfrey was much used by medical men in the seventeenth and eighteenth centuries for those 'Bursten Within', i.e. in cases of haematemesis and haemotypsis. They had much faith in it. Was this justified? No doubt much would depend on the nature of the diseases concerned. Some would probably be ulcers in the stomach and duodenum, others were possibly malignant growths. In chest cases they evidently treated phthisical haemorrhages with it.

In the course of the past twenty years there have been many opportunities for testing the situation, and one can only infer that whereas there are cases of internal ulcerative conditions in which improvement has been noted, there have been a good many in which the results were doubtful. One can only speak with any degree of certainty when diagnosis has been clear and where beneficial results have not followed other forms of medical treatment. One such experience occurred in the case of an elderly man who after suffering pain after food, vomiting of blood, melaena and other clinical evidences of ulceration which were unrelieved by medical treatment, finally submitted to operation. He nearly died on the table after the stomach, having a very evident ulcer in it, had been exposed. The operation had to be abandoned and so far as local conditions were concerned he remained *in statu quo ante*. He was then treated with allantoin dissolved in a comfrey infusion and a purely milk diet was prescribed, with the result that he was free from signs and symptoms in a month and is still alive at 90 odd years of age.

There have been good results and uncertain ones in cases of gastric and duodenal ulcers, but my general impression is that allantoin and comfrey are useful adjuncts to general dietetic treatment.

The following extreme case suggests that allantoin may find useful application in gastric and other internal ulcerations:

On 17 February, 1911, a woman, aged 47, was admitted into my ward in an extremely debilitated condition in consequence of a severe attack of haematemesis. For many weeks previously she had suffered from pain after food, and had vomited persistently for a fortnight prior to her admission. Even water caused pain and was immediately rejected. There had been melaena for some time prior to the attack of haematemesis for which she was immediately admitted. For twelve months she had been conscious of pain on

pressure over the abdomen, and had noticed a lump in the epi-
gastrium and extending into the right hypochondrium. This
woman was so feeble that the ward sister said that she thought it
was a pity that a patient so ill and advanced in disease should be
sent into the hospital. I felt disposed to agree with this opinion,
because on examining her abdomen I found a tumour just under-
neath the ribs on the right side. It was rounded, irregular, and
intensely painful, and my feeling at the time was that she had a
carcinoma involving the stomach, and this opinion was
strengthened by the fact that she had an undoubted carcinoma of
the breast. When the irritability of the stomach subsided she
was given the mucilaginous infusion of comfrey root reinforced
with some of the saturated solution of allantoin. In addition to the
improvement which took place in her stomach symptoms, in the
course of a month the abdominal tumour disappeared, an area
remaining, however, which was extremely painful on pressure;
but in time this also disappeared, and what I had taken to be a
malignant growth had vanished.

I have treated other cases of gastric and duodenal ulcers in the
same way, and have reason to believe that it is a helpful measure
for them.

RELATION OF ALLANTOIN AS A
CELL-PROLIFERANT IN CASES OF MALIGNANCY

Having demonstrated that allantoin is a substance capable of being
utilized both by vegetable and animal cells in connection with
their proliferative processes, the next point to determine was
whether it produced any influence upon malignant cell-growth. A
good many cases have been recorded where cancerous, or sarcomatous growths are reputed to have been benefited by treatment
with comfrey. They are mentioned among the 'vertues' in some of
the old Herbals. We have a modern example in the case referred to
by Professor William Thompson (p. 181), and there have been
others which led to our trying the effect of comfrey and allantoin
when applied locally in cases of advanced and ulcerating cancerous
growths. Except in the case of rodent ulcer referred to on p. 190,

no definite signs of improvement were noted. Whether consequent mitotic changes took place was not determined, and so far as at present observed it can only be stated that comfrey and allantoin do not appear to have any capacity for producing a somatic cell from a malignant one, or a carcinomatous or sarcomatous cell from a somatic one, and no reasonable explanation can be afforded for the occasional cures which have followed their employment.

From its influences on normal cells it can only be inferred that since allantoin leads to their proliferation it may possibly have something to do with the activities of nucleic acid. If this is the case a study of the structure and building up of nucleic acid may in the future prove to be of some importance. It was at one time believed that it consisted of four metaphosphoric acid residues, each linked to a pentose molecule (the sugar ribose) and to one molecule respectively of the purine bases adenine and guanine, and one each of the pyrimidine derivatives thymine and cytosine. It is to the two purine bases that allantoin may be indirectly related, since they both yield uric acid in the course of their chemical metabolism, whilst uric acid when suitably oxidized yields allantoin. Nucleic acid and sodium nucleate have for some time been known to increase the count of white blood-corpuscles in cases of pneumonia, and it has been supposed that the indirect relationship of allantoin to nucleic acid may to some extent be responsible for this. Dr. Titherley informs me that it is now generally believed that the phosphoric acid residue in nucleic acid is that of common ortho-phosphoric acid and that Levene now considers that the four nucleotides (phosphoric—pentose sugar—purine—pyrimidine) are linked through the pentose groupings thus:

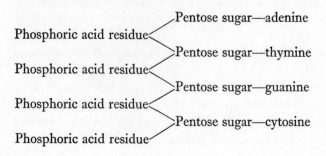

Phosphoric acid residue⟨ Pentose sugar—adenine

Phosphoric acid residue⟨ Pentose sugar—thymine

Phosphoric acid residue⟨ Pentose sugar—guanine

Phosphoric acid residue⟨ Pentose sugar—cytosine

This is contrary to Kossel's formulation of the phosphoric acid residues as being linked together themselves, also each being independently linked to the pentose sugar. Another authority (W. Jones) does not link the phosphoric acid residues either in the manner of Kossel or of Levene but links the pentose sugar residues together (not through phosphoric acid) and each independently to a phosphoric acid residue, leaving each phosphoric acid residue to contain two hydroxyl groups. Levene's formulation gives one hydroxyl group in three of the residues and two in the fourth.

It seems reasonable to suppose that cellular stability may depend upon the efficient building-up of nucleic acid, and as some of the experiments on plants have suggested, this probably results from a metabolic process in the cells. On this account there would appear to be little use in giving or applying nucleic acid (or nucleo-protein) when it is desired to build up that protein in the cells. It seems likely that they cannot make use of the fully formed material but require to assimilate the constituents required for cellular growth, structure and stability. On this account experiments might be directed towards the discovery of the effects upon cell growth of the various constituents of nucleic acid.

As previously stated, the connection between nucleic acid and allantoin is a very indirect one, and there is no real evidence that the latter builds up the adenine and guanine components of nucleic acid. At present this is in the realms of hypothesis.

The only substances which have been experimented with up to the present have been meta- and ortho-phosphoric acids which in dilute solutions ($\frac{1}{2}$ to 1 per cent) have certainly been found useful in the treatment of old sinuses and abscess cavities which were showing little signs of closing. The results of washing them out with these solutions have proved very satisfactory.

Finally, a survey of the results of using decoctions of the *Symphytum officinale* and solutions of allantoin in cases of alleged malignancy brings out the suggestive observation that nearly every case in which benefit seemed to ensue was treated either with the decoctions alone or sometimes with the addition of small amounts of allantoin. In Professor Thompson's case the patient inferred that the growth was dispersed by the local application of comfrey poultices. The case of rodent ulcer which improved so greatly was treated in the first place with comfrey mucilage and afterwards with allantoin extracted from the rhizome. The woman suffering from an apparently malignant growth involving the stomach cleared up under the administration of a mucilaginous decoction of the rhizome reinforced with the synthetic allantoin.

These and other cases, not recorded in the text, lead to the conjecture as to the possibility that the optically active *d*-allantoin in the comfrey and other vegetable and animal structures may have biological influences on cells different from or accessory to, those produced by the synthetic (racemic) product which, whoever, undoubtedly acts as a cell-proliferant and promotes healing as heretofore described. By analogy it may be surmised that natural products are superior to their synthetic isomers in their biochemical activities. Take for example the case of glucose of which the optically active *d*-form is an essential element in metabolism, whereas the synthetic *l*-glucose is not valuable as food stuff. The difference between the natural *d*-glucose and its image-isomer *l*-glucose is of the same type as that between the *d*- and *l*-allantoins (i.e. in optical activity and asymmetric arrangement of atoms). In all chemical properties they are (in both cases) identical, yet biochemically the two forms of glucose are completely different and it seems possible that some difference in biochemical activity may also exist in the case of the allantoins. Practical experience tells us that synthetic allantoin is an active agent, but the question arises as to whether the natural form found in the allantois, in milk, and in various vegetable structures may not possess virtues superior to those of its synthetic isomer.

For all we know allantoin may have some physiological association with other elements found in the animal or plant such as endocrines or vitamin B_1, which may influence its therapeutic properties. One striking point connected with its action is the relatively small amount required in solution to set going a local healing process, e.g. by application to an ulcer or a multiplication of leucocytes in the blood which will be referred to presently, in this respect resembling a hormone.

This ends the primary investigation concerning the *Symphytum officinale* and its contained allantoin, much of which was published in the *British Medical Journal* (6 January and 21 September, 1912).

Further Observations Concerning Allantoin, 1914–1935

In connection with the local application of allantoin to septic and sloughing surfaces, attention has been directed to the 'cleaning-up' process which takes place as a preliminary to, or concomitantly with, the ingrowth of epithelial cells from the margins of ulcers and from the islets of epithelium on the surface of burns. This was originally ascribed only to an increase in the vitality or resistance in the cells themselves, but the point arose as to whether this might not be brought about, in part at any rate, by some change in the cellular environment. That the cleaning-up did not result from a chemical antiseptic itself, and by the circumstances that many of the ulcers had failed to clean up or heal when treated by various antiseptics before the solution of allantoin had been applied. The question thus arose as to whether this lessening or inhibition of sepsis resulted from a promotion of phagocytosis.

Some light was thrown by Drs. Albert Berthelot and D. M. Bertrand in a research carried out in the Pasteur Institute, the results of which were published in August 1912.* This research was promoted by their notice of my publication in the *British Medical Journal*, 6 January, 1912. It had occurred to them that allantoin might act by stimulation of phagocytosis, and they studied its action by experiment on guinea-pigs.

Three cubic centimetres of a saturated solution of allantoin were injected into the peritoneal cavity of a guinea-pig. Eighteen hours afterwards they detected the presence of a light peritoneal exudate containing polynuclear cells. In order to obtain a more abundant leucocytosis 10 cgm. of finely pulverized allantoin were suspended in 5 c.c. of water, which after sterilization was injected into the peritoneal cavities of two animals, and twenty hours later a discharge of purulent liquid, composed entirely of absolutely aseptic polynuclear cells, was withdrawn by means of a fine pipette. They

* *Comptes Rendus Hebdomadaires des Séances de la Société de Biologie*, lxxiii, 2 August, 1912, p. 263.

then injected similar allantoin suspensions into several other guinea-pigs, varying in weight from 350 to 400 grm., and twenty-four hours afterwards, having determined the presence of a very abundant peritoneal exudate, they injected into one of them a fatal dose of a young culture of cholera vibrio, and into the other a similar fatal dose of Eberth's bacillus. Control animals were injected at the same time with similar fatal doses.

All the control animals died in from twelve to nineteen hours, whereas the animals which had received the allantoin were un-affected and survived. The peritoneal exudate taken from these latter animals, twenty hours after the injection of the microbes, was sterile, and was composed of leucocytes, some few of which contained granules, which might have been the debris of dead bacteria. From these experiments the authors concluded that allantoin was capable of strengthening the local resistance of the peritoneum against infection and of causing considerable leucocytosis and they suggested that the favourable action of allantoin was probably attributable, in part at all events, to this.

These experiments, and the observations made by clinicians concerning the cleaning-up of septic surfaces, opened up a new field of inquiry, for it seemed possible that if the local application of allantoin promoted a multiplication of phagocytes, it might also, if introduced into the blood, set up a general leucocytosis, and that if this proved to be the case a controlling influence might be exerted on infective diseases, and especially perhaps in those types of cases where there is a controlled immunity. It is well known for instance that immunity from pneumonia is diminished when other diseases such as influenza (in which, by the way, there is a leucopoenia) lower the vital resistance. This resistance, strange to say, is diminished in some conditions which improve the general health. We seldom come across pneumonia among sailors or passengers when they are at sea. It is on arriving at the ports when their leucocytes are off guard that they are liable to become victims. Everybody recognizes how prone we are to get catarrhal colds after arrival in towns from a sea voyage or from a holiday in a relatively germ-free atmosphere. This tendency to infection was recognized by the physicians of a past generation. I recollect the late Dr. William Carter about forty years ago warning me, on my suggestion of Spitzbergen for a holiday, that there was a risk of becoming infected with pneumonia on returning to my hospital work. At that time, however, I do not think that the function of the leucocytes as infection-preventers was much understood.

Pneumonia is to some extent an unsatisfactory disease on which to make unambiguous observations because severe cases often recover, whatever treatment may be adopted, and there is also the fact that the strain of pneumonia organism prevalent at one period may differ in virulence from that of another.

It so happened that the first suitable cases which came before me for observation were severe lobar pneumonias, and it will be best to record the history of this clinical investigation which was commenced in 1914, in order of sequence. One of the earliest cases treated made a somewhat unexpected recovery. The patient, a quarter-master on one of the liners, was desperately ill and his blood had a very low leucocyte count, only about 6,000 per c.m.m., a point which always makes for a bad prognosis in the later stages of pneumonia. There was a possibility of there being a small amount of fluid in his chest, and thinking that its removal might help matters I needled the chest but got nothing but blood from the solidified lung. Without removing the needle I then slowly injected 2 c.c. of an 0·5 per cent sterile solution of allantoin into the solid lung. Within two hours the leucocyte count had gone up to 15,000; later it was 20,000 and with this increment there was distinct improvement and a speedy crisis. A possible explanation, however, in a case of this kind is the fact that a simple puncture of the lung will sometimes precipitate a crisis and in some chronic types will similarly promote resolution. I pointed this out long ago in a paper entitled 'Puncture of the Lung in Chronic Pneumonic Conditions.'*

In order to eliminate the possible influences of lung puncture, I proceeded to give my patient allantoin by hypodermic injection, and was encouraged to a certain extent by what appeared to be resultant benefits. For instance, in the case of a man, aged 23,

* Published in the *Liverpool Med. Chir. Journal* of March, 1901.

whose leucocyte count in the later stage of the disease was 9,000 per c.m.m., 2 c.c. of the 0·5 per cent solution of allantoin was given hypodermically. In two hours the count had risen to 12,000 and after another injection it went up to about 20,000 and remained high until the crisis occurred. Such cases were encouraging but there were admittedly a considerable number of failures and one could by no means speak with certainty as to what might accrue from this method of treatment.

The point was that at that period I was only using allantoin as a kind of *dernier ressort* in the later stages of grave or apparently hopeless cases presenting indications of serious toxaemia. Many of these cases already exhibited a considerable leucocytosis which was not materially influenced by allantoin, and the unsatisfactory results were due to cardiac failure brought about by the toxaemia. In consequence of this, the use of allantoin was abandoned in these grave cases; the fact remained, however, that it had conferred benefit in some cases presenting a low count, and this led to an entire change of procedure which resulted in a very different course of events. The allantoin was now given in the earliest instead of the later stages of the disease, and for the efficient clinical observations of these cases I am greatly indebted to Dr. Edward Blair Wilkinson, who was my Resident at the time, and to my student Mr. N. Green, who took a great interest in the subject and read his thesis for the Cambridge degree on it.

Allantoin and Leucocytosis

The first experiments were carried out in normal healthy individuals, to whom a grain of allantoin in solution was given by mouth at two-hourly intervals on an empty stomach. The counts were generally taken two hours after each of three successive doses. The polynuclear cells were increased by from 5 to 15 per cent, and it was noted by making subsequent counts that they had returned to the normal in from sixteen to forty-eight hours.

Next came the administration of allantoin in cases of pneumonia commencing at the earliest possible periods after the onset of the disease, with the result that a rapid increase in the number of leucocytes was generally observed. In many cases it was noted that the crisis was early, this being influenced by the shortness of the period, following the onset of the disease prior to the administration of allantoin. For instance, in nine cases where the crisis took place on or before the seventh day the allantoin had been given within the first seventy-two hours, whereas in six cases in which it had been commenced after the first seventy-two hours the crisis occurred on or after the eighth day.

A very striking instance of the benefit resulting from early administration was in a patient who had been operated on for gallstones. He had a sudden rise of temperature with rigor, pain at the base of the left chest, where there were undoubted signs of early pulmonary consolidation including impairment of the percussion note, bronchial breathing and some fine crepitant sounds. No blood-count was taken but allantoin was given intensively, 2 gr. in solution at two-hourly intervals, and within forty-eight hours the temperature was normal and the condition practically cleared up. In another case which I saw at the Bourton-on-the-Water hospital in 1933, where a pneumonia had commenced in a very stormy way, accompanied by pericarditis, a similar speedy resolution took place, but was followed by an empyema. Empyema has on several occasions followed in cases of pneumonia treated with allantoin, and a conjecture has arisen as to the possibility of it resulting from what may be called a hyper-leucocytosis.*

With reference to the period of crisis Mr. Green recorded that out of 15 cases of frank lobar pneumonia treated with allantoin during a period of twelve months, the crises occurred as follows:

One case on the 4th day
One case on the 5th day
Five cases on the 6th day
Two cases on the 7th day
Three cases on the 8th day
One case on the 11th day
Two cases on the 12th day

In nine of these cases the crisis occurred on or before the seventh day, and in six of them on or after the eighth day. In the former

* With Dr. Leslie King.

group the allantoin was given, with two exceptions well within the first seventy-two hours from the onset, and in the latter group after the first seventy-two hours, with three exceptions, one of which was a very severe case with involvement of almost the whole of both lungs.

A point to note in connection with the course of pneumonias treated with allantoin (also observed by Mr. Green) is the occurrence of a pseudo-crisis generally from twenty to thirty hours after the drug was first given, the temperature dropping to normal and remaining so for a few hours, but without much relief from symptoms. Occasionally one or two such falls in temperature preceded the true crisis. Mr. Green suggested that the pseudo-crisis might be explained by an abnormally rapid increase in the leucocytes causing a temporary check to the multiplication of pneumococci and production of their toxins in the blood stream enabling the thermal centre to regain its balance for a while. The symptoms are not abated during the pseudo-crisis because the lung condition remains unchanged, and the disordered circulation in the lung does not enable many of the newly formed leucocytes to penetrate and attack its contained pneumococci.

That allantoin renders a useful service in pneumonia is indicated by the relatively low mortality of patients treated with it as compared with the general run of cases treated on the usual therapeutic principals. At the time when Mr. Green worked in this investigation there were ample opportunities for making comparative observations. Over a period of two years 47 cases of lobar pneumonia had been treated in the hospital, and in that period most of the cases in my own wards had been given allantoin but very few of those in other wards. At any period in those two years the cases would be of somewhat similar strains, or at all events they would be fairly evenly mixed. Twenty-five of the 47 cases were treated on the usual therapeutic lines, the remaining 22 cases were given allantoin by mouth, some of them with such additional medicines as might be required to meet symptoms. The mortality in the former group was 20 per cent, whereas in the latter it was under 5 per cent.

Making all allowances for conditions which might influence

prognosis such as questions of age, precedent or collateral infections, etc., it seems evident that there must have been some
relationship between the diminished mortality and the administration of allantoin.

During the past eight years Dr. Robert Stewart and other
medical men practising in and around Bourton-on-the-Water,
without making any leucocyte counts, treated their pneumonias
both in and out of hospital on the principles above referred to, and
their experiences have been definitely satisfactory.

During the past three years (1932–35) a series of clinical
observations have been made with allantoin with a view to confirm-
ing or otherwise the presumption that it produces a leucocytosis
when administered by mouth. In 1932 I sent a quantity of the
crystals, which had been in my possession for a year or more, to
Dr. Norman Capon of Liverpool, and his former Resident, Dr.
O. Vaughan Jones, kindly carried out a series of investigations, the
general results of which were distinctly confirmatory. The allantoin was given to 20 individuals whose leucocyte counts were
within normal limits.

To each of them he gave 2 gr. of allantoin dissolved in one
ounce of water at two-hourly intervals and, in order that the
leucocytosis following the ingestion of food should be eliminated
as far as possible the blood count in each case was made from two
and a half to three hours after a meal. By way of control, blood
counts were made in five cases under the same conditions, but
without giving any allantoin. In every one of the cases receiving
allantoin a leucocytosis ensued, ranging from 50 per cent to 83 per
cent increase in seven instances, and from 25 per cent to 47 per
cent in the remaining thirteen cases. None of the controls showed
appreciable changes. The average increase was somewhat low
compared with the results in some of my own original observations
and those of the staff in the pathological laboratory of the Royal
Southern Hospital, from ten to fifteen years ago, and one rather
suspected that the crystals of allantoin might have deteriorated.
It so happened that in 1934 I sent a supply of the same stock of
crystals to Dr. M. Schwartzman who was interested in the matter,
and he reported that in a limited number of observations his

results were not convincing. This led him to obtain some freshly prepared allantoin which he administered, in accordance with the recommended instructions, to 19 people who were either in normal health or the subjects of diseases presenting no blood changes, and in course of conversation he informed me that in 17 of them positive results, with between 59 and 65 per cent increase in the number of leucocytes were obtained.

It seems just possible, therefore, that synthetic allantoin crystals, although supposed to be quite stable, may deteriorate with keeping, and if so it is advisable to use crystals which are not too old kept absolutely dry in a well-stoppered bottle. It is at present uncertain how long they will keep in an unimpaired condition, but crystals freshly prepared seven months ago, so kept, have certainly proved perfectly active in a number of recently investigated bloods.

I have already explained that solutions should be made with distilled water, and that heat short of boiling should be employed in their preparation. It is advisable to powder the crystals finely first in a perfectly clean mortar, and then use only hot distilled water, stirring well to get the solid into solution, of course using a chemically clean glass test tube or beaker and glass rod.

In conclusion it may be said that although lobar pneumonia has been the disease mainly investigated with reference to the action of allantoin in producing phagocytosis, it may be useful in other infective conditions which might be benefited by the production of a leucocytosis. It has been found serviceable in some cases of broncho-pneumonia, and in some septic infections, and even the common cold seems sometimes to have been adverted when the drug has been given at the commencement. Its employment in the early stages of influenza and in other diseases associated with leucopaenia might be usefully investigated.

Its utility as a promoter of healing in wounds, ulcers, and sinuses has already been appreciated in this and other countries, and it is generally recognized that the best way of applying it is on sterilized lint or gauze without waterproof coverings. Ointments having lanoline bases which are capable of holding solutions of allantoin have proved useful.

A curious suggestion has recently come from America,* following the discovery made by entomologists of the U.S. Department of Agriculture, that maggots of certain flies when placed on wounds promote their healing. In this connection Dr. William Robinson, of the Bureau of Entomology and Plant Quarantine, found that allantoin given off by the maggots is responsible for at least a part of the healing power they possess, and the article goes on to state that surgeons who have found it difficult in the past to obtain sterile maggots laud the discovery that allantoin, which is spoken of as a new treatment, can be made to control healing.

The impression gained as to the cell-proliferating property of allantoin is that it acts like a hormone, in the sense that such small quantities of it set going proliferations of considerable magnitude.

Preparation and Administration of Allantoin Solution

For internal administration or local application of allantoin it is essential to use freshly prepared solutions of which the most convenient strength is 0·4 per cent. This is approximately 2 grains to the ounce. Allantoin is very sensitive to the action of alkalis, and on this account distilled water should be used for making the solutions.

Although prolonged heating decomposes allantoin, it has been found that water just below the boiling point may be used for dissolving it without appreciable decomposition, provided the solution is quickly cooled.

Another point to remember is that though it is generally supposed that the crystals are quite stable and may be kept for any length of time, clinical experience has indicated that they are apt to lose their efficiency if kept too long. Care should therefore be taken to use crystals which are not too old and which have been safeguarded against damp by keeping them in well-stoppered bottles. They appear to remain stable for at least four months, and probably considerably longer if kept perfectly dry.

Solutions of allantoin should be freshly prepared in sufficient quantity for use during a period not exceeding twenty-four hours.

Experiments on plants in which older solutions have been used have shown that they are less active than freshly prepared ones.

* *Drug Trade News*, 29 April, 1935.

11. The future of comfrey

About a hundred years after Henry Doubleday became a comfrey grower, comfrey growing exploded in the United States, where in 1974 there were sixty-five-acre fields and thousand-acre plantings planned. What made these possible was the exploitation of the system used in Africa of root cutting planting.

The late Elmer Deetz of Canby, Oregon, became the Vernon Stephenson of America, buying his stock from Bodie Seeds Ltd. of Canada, from the original import that brought the ton of lucerne seed that began the H.D.R.A. and from which all the comfrey in North America has been grown. Elmer Deetz was an enthusiast, and like many enthusiasts he talked comfrey and he sold comfrey, but took its cultivation little further. A great many other growers began to sell comfrey, and through the 1960s their advertisements blossomed in *Organic Gardening and Farming*, the one organic movement periodical in the world, with a circulation of 850,000 a month. Articles appeared, largely quoting *Russian Comfrey*, H.D.R.A. material, and herbal works, and meeting hostility from orthodox agricultural research.

It was not possible to import the Bocking clones (though some No. 14s grown from a single plant sent by air letter post are thriving in Seattle) because the U.S. Plant Health Authorities insist not only on every consignment satisfying the most rigorous inspection in Britain, but they fumigate it on arrival so thoroughly that the roots are entirely destroyed. There have been attempts to sort out the clones in America but there is no recognized standard and it is hoped that the descriptions of these at the beginning of this book will help at least to eliminate low yielders from U.S. stocks.

This gave all American comfrey growers a huge but hidden advantage, for this drastic policy kept comfrey rust out of the U.S. as effectively as their Food and Drug Administration Authority

218

prevented the import of thalidomide and saved their children from the tragic deformities that this tranquillizer spread over Europe. Even if *Melampsorella symphyti* did manage to sneak across, as rabies may in a film star's lovingly smuggled dog, *Symphytum officinale* does not grow wild in America. Comfrey's inability to set seed prevented it from joining the weeds of Old England that crossed in seed corn cleaned only to Pilgrim Fathers' standards of purity, which now compete with the goldenrod beside the multi-lane Interstate Highways.

So America has comfrey with all its growth potential un-handicapped by the debilitating disease that has infected so many British stocks. For the sake of the contribution comfrey can make to a protein-hungry world, we can hope that the exports of roots that will be needed in the 1980s will be made from the U.S.A. and Japan, for the stocks in both countries are the agricultural equivalent to the New Zealand Strain of Lloyd George raspberries, that were found free from virus and reintroduced to British gardens.

The American comfrey explosion began when one of the sellers had the idea of 'leasing' comfrey plantings. Fields, at first of only an acre or two, were sold to small farmers with a signed and witnessed agreement that the root cutting crop would be bought back every third or even second year. Then a potato digger would be run along the rows taking up the roots to about ten inches deep. These roots would be cut up into $1\frac{1}{2}$ inch long sections, bagged and sent by road or rail to customers as easily as seed potatoes.

They were planted usually 18 inches between root cuttings and three feet between rows, often with a strawberry planter or other machine to put them in accurately and at speed. There was no need to bother about getting the crown just below the surface— the root cuttings lay flat about three inches down, just as they do in a British nursery, but instead of being grown for a year in foot apart rows, they were harvested so cheaply that enough for an acre cost only three hundred dollars in 1974, compared with £240 for plants to put in a British acre (roughly five hundred dollars) while planting costs made a field that was clean to start with cost about six hundred dollars.

This method had an advantage on cost, but still makes weeding far more of a problem, for though a shallow discing or harrowing or a pre-emergent weedkiller for inorganic farmers (as many U.S. comfrey growers are) can clear the first batch of seedlings, leaving the growing root cuttings safely below danger, weeds are a constant problem.

Mr. Elmer Jeskey of Aurora, Oregon, one of the best of the modern U.S. comfrey growers, has solved this by using a 60-inch Rotavator with the middle tines taken out, drawn by an old Ferguson tractor which starts so easily that cleaning the crop is as easy as picking up a hoe. The gap in the middle fits over the growing plants and the remaining tines cultivate a 14-inch wide strip on either side. Machines have been built to order for this job, but merely removing the tines is cheapest and as effective. The advantage of using a Rotavator is that its action throws the soil flat, instead of making a ridge beside the plants which interferes with mechanized cutting. Weeds still grow between the plants in the rows, but the crop can hold them down to some extent, though hand hoeing is advisable. It is possible with 18-inch planting to fit the tines over the plants and cultivate the other way, but it is tight. Twenty inches would be better, but in America the importance of the weed problem is not fully appreciated.

If the roots are lifted every two years it is possible to use shallow rotavation to clean the field all over, bearing in mind the problem that every fragment of root will grow, so tines should be kept well above the cut ends, and a Rotavator without any tines removed should be used. This type of machine is far better than the horse-hoes of Old England even as late as the 1940s, because its action lets air into the soil, leaving the ground 'puffed', and this dries out the short sections of couch grass (*Agropyrum repens*) root, providing this operation can be carried out in summer with dry weather, and repeated at intervals about three weeks apart.

The cut roots come through again in as little as a month in summer, but this treatment reduces the yield of foliage so greatly that it is not honest to quote British or even American figures from established plants as representing the production from a field dug up every other year, in some cases, to provide roots for sale, which have become the main crop, so far as profit is concerned.

The major problem of the 'leasing' system is that it can become a kind of pyramid selling operation. An acre planted with about 7,000 root cuttings will produce about 140,000 when it is lifted in the third year, and nearer 200,000 in the sixth when it seems to stabilize, but the system has not been going long enough to be sure of the life span of a constantly lifted crop. So each acre must have twenty acres of sales in its third season, and those twenty acres demand four hundred three years ahead, plus another twenty-five for the first acre. Another three years brings 85,000 acres, every one of which is multiplying and remultiplying twenty-fold every third season, with a probable life of twelve years. All these growers have contracts with the middlemen who supply the sales service and the planting expertise, and all are indignant when their roots are not sold. The salesmen work harder and harder (America has some of the hardest working salesmen in the world), hastening the day when they will face a million angry farmers with their contracts broken and the whole United States one solid comfrey planting from coast to coast.

In England in the 1890s, when Thomas Christy was the first of the comfrey promoters, the high price of plants limited the boom to those who could afford to plant trial areas, like the Reverend E. Highton of Bude and the others who never wrote to *The Field*, the *Gardeners Chronicle* or *The Country Gentleman's Magazine*. In the U.S. farmers can afford to put down 50 acres or more of comfrey, and with a really high pressure salesman pushing hard enough, many will plant a huge area with little idea how they are going to use the production.

As in every country, the good fields are always owned by the man who is feeding his stock and making a profit, and one of these is Elmer Jeskey who modified his Rotavator and keeps his six acres clean, fed, and cut, as in England. He feeds pedigree Aberdeen Angus calves to sell at eight months old, supplementing their grazing with a daily comfrey ration which gives him an average live weight gain of 100 lb. more in eight months than he would get on grass alone. The high mineral and high protein feed gives perfect condition of coat, vigour and bone structure, which counts when better prices are paid on market days.

Daily harvesting is with a small silorator discharging into a
high-sided trailer, both towed by an old Case tractor, which makes
this operation as easy as taking a scythe off its hook in the barn, for
it is time saved on daily operations that adds up on the farm. It
pays to have old, easy-starting tractors ready hitched for this kind
of operation, and the trailer is made large enough to hold the
biggest daily ration in one load, in one trip up and back down a
long comfrey field. This shape is quite important because it means
less turning and headland space than on a square plot.

In 1973 Elmer Jeskey made hay with his third cut, leaving it
three days to dry in windrows and taking it up with an ordinary
pick-up bailer. It dries black, rather like 'rooftop hay' but is
palatable for stock and it is fed as a supplement in the early
spring. Making comfrey hay for baling, like all hay making, is a
matter of watching the weather and knowing when it is ready to
bale.

The calves are brought in, and they fit the growing period of
comfrey perfectly, with their maximum appetites in the autumn,
and no stock in the winter, which avoids the need for conservation.
The manure comes from a turkey ranch up the road where over a
million birds are grown for Christmas, Thanksgiving, and the in-
between sales that make Beltsville Whites a fast grown source of
protein with a big market in the U.S.A. It is spread from a trailer
in dusty flakes from the trodden surface of the turkey yards, and
costs nothing but the fetching. The cattle manure is, of course,
dropped on the pastures which the transfer of fertility from the
comfrey is constantly enriching. A large part of the profit is still
in the root sales, but Mr. Jeskey can at least show the buyers how
to feed comfrey to stock and make the other two-thirds of the
money.

If 100 head of calves can be fed off six acres, then sixty acres
should feed 1,000. Therefore large plantings can only be justified
where there is a ready industrial use. In the U.S.A. there are a
number of experiments under way with cubers and pelleters, both
of which dry the crop under pressure and convert it to a high
protein cattle cake or pig nut. The problem is to bring the inventor
to the grower with the acreage, before the acres go under weeds

and are ploughed up by the farmer who does not know how to use his production.

Perhaps the most promising development in comfrey utilization is the bacterial process discovered by Mr. Robert Teas of Othello Washington. He was one of many farmers with thirty acres which he allowed to get weedy from shortage of labour, and failed to irrigate enough in his dry climate in Eastern Washington. Before he gave up, and concentrated on repairing irrigation machinery, he experimented with comfrey foliage and produced a black substance rather like Marmite or Vecon. The bacteria used are cellulose breakers; they reduce the fibre to maltose and fructose, producing some heat that dries out about half the moisture, and concentrating the remaining substances into a soluble substrate which will dissolve in water. The sample available to the H.D.R.A. was too small for a full analysis of the amino-acids or the minerals and allantoin, but the complete breakdown of the fibre showed that although the allantoin inhibits bacterial action so the substance kept for nearly a year in an ordinary screwtop jar, it did not stop the process before the fibre was finished.

Its analysis was as follows:

	Percentage
Moisture	42·33
Ash	24·38
Protein (Nx 6·25)	7·45
Oil (Acid Hydrolysis)	3·64
Carbohydrate (by difference)	22·20
Fibre	Nil

Comparison with other foodstuffs

	Vitamin B12 p.p.m.
Comfrey Teas process	0·052
Sheep's heart	0·052
Eggs	0·020
Lean Beef	0·014
Beef Liver	0·800
Mutton	0·021

The analysis was made on 24 September by Messrs. Aynsome Laboratories of Grange-over-Sands, Lancs., who did the first B12 analysis in 1959. Now they have analysed the first vegetable product to beat beef and mutton, and to equal hearts, but not by a long way to equal liver. The comparative figures are from 'Pantothenic Acid, Vitamin B.6 and Vitamin B.12 in Foods' by Martha Lois Orr, U.S. Dept. Agriculture 1969.

Mr. Teas has given comfrey its first food processing industry potential, for until now comfrey tea, comfrey flour and dried comfrey root have all depended on small scale hand picking, high labour cost, and high price production, for the medicinal and health food market. His small 'digester' and garden shed scale apparatus could one day be the basis of a continuous flow process taking cut comfrey, thick stems, midribs and all, just as they are shot off the endless stream of trailers from April till the end of October, from those thousand-acre fields. His substance would probably be easiest to develop as a poultry food, entirely replacing fishmeal, especially for turkeys, and a dog and cat food in the U.S.A. where the protein that should stay in hungry countries to feed children goes to produce one-ninth as much food in 'finger lickin' good' fried chicken. This lies far ahead at the end of a long road of research, far beyond the capacity of genius in a garden shed.

Today food chemists talk of 'knitting steaks' by spinning soya beans into fibres and building them into an imitation meat, with an excellent balance of amino-acids, and entirely synthetic flavours. 'Knit' from comfrey and you have $3\frac{1}{2}$ *tons* from a 100-ton an acre crop, spread through the year where the day length is equal on the Equator where the tight belt of hunger grips the world.

There are a number of cellulose-breaking bacteria that could use the fibre in comfrey, which makes it unsuitable for human food, to add carbohydrate and partly dry it without fuel. For in the future that is science fact rather than science fiction, energy is all important, and though we may make cattle feed protein from natural gas and crude oil, these may well be better burned than converted into synthetic foods. Robert Teas has demonstrated that the Vitamin B12 in comfrey is not just a chance contamination, but something which can be concentrated to a worthwhile quantity, in human food. His invention could be used to make a spread like Marmite or Vecon, a soup stock which should even jellify if the amino-acids are concentrated but unchanged, an addition to a maize porridge which will supply the missing amino acids and B12 that bean and maize diets lack, and it could dry to a powder for easy transport to famine or disaster areas.

It would also be the easiest form yet in which to take allantoin, and could be the basis of a whole range of medicinal advances, once the research has been done. Science consists of asking nature questions one at a time and measuring the answers, but unless there is likely to be a tin, a bottle or a factory chimney in that answer, science today does not ask the questions. Mr. Teas may have found the factory chimney that Henry Doubleday glimpsed a hundred years ago, when he tried to make gum for those Penny Blacks.

The answer may be a yeast that will grow on green foliage, and a Torula yeast is under trial in Japan, while several Candida strains are under consideration in other research projects. All look brighter now we know that the trace of cobalt in all comfrey foliage shows that B12 is always there, and that these biological processes do not break it down. Yeast can be good (but not very attractive) food, but it lacks B12 which comfrey has. How much else is preserved by the various processes only research will show.

Just as those who go down to the sea and find the beach coated with crude oil have to consider the consequences of quarter-million-ton oil tankers, when comfrey is industrialized we must think of how exactly we shall cope with those planned 1,000-acre comfrey fields. They will stretch as far as the eye can reach, hedgeless, treeless and weedless, unless we can breed a legume that will suppress grass and grow between the rows to fix nitrogen and check erosion. This is perhaps foremost among the many number one research priorities for comfrey that jostle for first place.

Cultivations like Elmer Jeskey's can be magnified, and there is no reason why those silorators and giant trailers should ever stop while the crop grows, their headlights showing them crawling through the night as the factory works round the clock. But farms, like factories, may find that the magic which the modern world finds in millions, can be black magic.

8

Vitamin B12 is synthetized by the digestive bacteria in earth-worms, and if we destroy those worms by chemical fertilizers, or systemic fungicides such as Benlate (which is quite effective against comfrey rust), down goes the value of the crop. In the fuel-short future, when the five tons of coal-equivalent it takes to make one ton of nitrogen fertilizer becomes all important, and when the energy to make superphosphate or refine, bag and transport potash fertilizers is considered, we cannot afford to throw away any of the qualities of comfrey.

The crop will take crude sewage sludge and liquid farmyard manure even when it is dormant, so tanker sewage sludge as sprayed on pastures and stubbles by many local authorities in Britain and the U.S.A. could go on at the rate of between 6,000 and 12,000 gallons an acre. This would have to be low in metals because of the risk of their building up to toxic levels in the soil as the years went by. Alternatives would be farm slurry, and methane generator slurry, which would hold far more humus. All soils need humus, not only for moisture retention, crumb structure and all the usual reasons, but because earthworms need *energy* to drive them through the soil, bring subsoil fertility to the surface, and also provide that B12.

A giant comfrey field would be perhaps the most extreme example of monoculture in agricultural history, and its problem would be the adding up of its problems through the years. One of these might well be attack by nemotodes or eelworms, especially the migratory type to which the pyrethrum eelworm belongs, and though this species is not found in Britain or the U.S.A., *Praty-lenchus penetrans*, which can attack potatoes, apple trees and strawberry plants, could change its habits.

In practice there would be an optimum size that would suit a constant supply for a factory, grown on a rotation, perhaps one of ten years' comfrey, one year's free-range pigs, winter wheat undersown with a ley, and then four years' grass, or potatoes and other vegetables to give a rest to the soil.

It is also possible that these biological processes would lend themselves to small scale production, and the yeasts might well be as easy as home yoghourt making. Once the way is found it might be possible to fill a large dish with cut comfrey, dab a culture on it, put another dish on top and set them to warm in the sun for a day, and produce a high-protein food supplement from perhaps twenty plants in a back yard. Protein where hungry people need it is far more important than protein stacked at the sea ports with no roads or transport to move it.

We are inclined to think of the less attractive foods like yeasts grown on potato crisp factory wastes, or crude oil refuse, as unsuitable for sale in supermarkets but ideal for the underdeveloped countries, just as the Victorians believed in plain, cheap and wholesome meals for the working classes. Yet in the Irish Potato Famine of the 1840s—the first in history in which a million *white* people starved to death—while the charitable Victorians were handing out nourishing soups made from beef bones, or maize meal gruel, Ireland was exporting thousands of tons of meat, wheat, butter and bacon to England. More than enough to have fed all those hungry people.

By the same black magic of economics, Britain, the U.S.A. and the technologically advanced countries, draw the land-costly high-protein foods from the underdeveloped world on such as scale that 'aid' is only a fraction of what is taken. For the fishmeal that would enrich their bread, we give them stones—arms, aircraft and automobiles.

If every pig farmer in the temperate world fed comfrey to replace the vitamin B12 in that fishmeal for our factory farms, more children would be spared the malnutrition in the first two years of their lives which means permanent mental injury. The underdeveloped countries need the 'miracle money' of a saner economic system more than they need miracle rice.

Comfrey too is a miracle crop, especially according to those who sell it and oversell it. But it is important that knowledge of how to use it and conserve it, as well as how to grow it, should not make it one more mechanized monoculture crop to make the rich richer and the poor poorer still. It could be a crop to build up the exhausted coffee lands of Brazil and to put high-protein food into the fields of small farmers everywhere, if only we could win the knowledge of crops that can be fitted into the openings in the

ecology of all countries is vastly more important than nuclear
power stations whose wastes may enslave the future for a thousand
years.

The work of Dr. MacAllister is in this book as the basis on
which the medical research of the future can build, with the help
of the two appendices that follow.

The risk for comfrey is that its future will lie at the end of the
traditional road from a sales boom to a slump and a loss of interest
in neglected fields, grown with an ignorance that wastes their
value: then ploughed up, to become worse weeds than those that
hide the ruined crop. Already the first plot to grow 100 tons an acre
in the United States, at the University of California, Davis, is
dry, weedy and neglected.

Maybe in fifty years time someone will be searching the back
files of the *San Francisco Examiner*, the *Sacramento Bee*, *The
Oregon Farmer* and the *Seattle Times* and track down my part in
the Great American Comfrey Boom of the 1970s, just as I followed
the British boom that began a hundred years ago through *The
Field*, *The Times*, the *Gardeners Chronicle* and the *Journal of the
Royal Agricultural Society of England*. Then they will start the
cycle all over again, perhaps angry with the correspondent in the
Cleveland Plain Dealer who pleads for someone to tell him how to
kill the comfrey he has ruined by ignorance, in the year 2000.

I hope that this book will help the future of comfrey to lie along
this first road, and that those who are concerned, as Henry was,
and I still am, that this crop should feed a world that can still be
hungry though its rockets reach the stars, will write to me for the
latest news of this plant that has grown so deeply into my life and
now grows faster and deeper still into the lives of others.

Appendix 1

The alkaloid content of comfrey
by Dr. D. B. Long, Ph.D., M.A.

Introduction

Alkaloids are organic substances other than certain simple amines and amino-acids associated with proteins which are produced by certain plants and which have a basic nitrogen atom. Although alkaloids may be regarded as metabolic by-products, they frequently serve the plant as a nitrogen reserve. They are widely distributed throughout the plant kingdom, being present in about 5 per cent of all species, and occur in a wide variety of chemical forms. Many of the alkaloids are pharmacologically active being either poisonous or having medicinal properties. Thus green potatoes produce a poisonous solanine, certain poppies—morphine, nux vomica—strychnine, tobacco—nicotine, and foxgloves—digitalis, and alkaloids are frequently the active component in herbal medicines.

One group of alkaloids known as the pyrrolizidines has come into prominence more recently. This group is hepatoxic, causing in the liver either acute reactions with massive necrosis (that is, total destruction of tissues) or slower chronic symptoms of wasting with the development of extensive liver tumours according to the level and duration of ingestion. This type of alkaloid is responsible for wasting and fatalities which occur in cattle grazing in fields containing *senecio* species (Ragwort) of the compositae. Other examples of the pyrrolizidine alkaloids also occur in Crotalaria (Leguminosae), Heliotropium (Boraginaceae) and many other species of plants from Graminaceae, Orchidaceae, Sapotaceae, etc. The pyrrolizidine group of alkaloids is generally considered to be highly toxic.

Comfrey belongs to the plant family of the Boraginaceae which includes the Heliotropium species with their high alkaloid content. Furthermore comfrey belongs to the subdivision of this family

(Tribe Anchusa) which contains *Anchusa officinalis* and *Borago officinalis* (L.) amongst others which are known to contain this alkaloid. It would be reasonable to expect therefore an alkaloid of this group to be present in comfrey and this has previously been found to be the case by others in *Symphytum perigrinum* (Ledeb) at a concentration of o·03 per cent. Nevertheless experience gained over many years with feeding cattle and horses on comfrey in different parts of the world has failed to produce any evidence of an acute reaction. Equally well there is an absence of any direct evidence of liver tumours of the chronic reaction in comfrey-fed animals having been observed in slaughter houses. However, from this negative indirect evidence it cannot be decisively concluded that comfrey does not present the toxic hazard of a chronic reaction because cattle bred for meat are slaughtered early in life when at their prime and long before the chronic reaction develops later in life following the slow accumulation of alkaloid. Thus with the fairly recent isolation and identification of two separate pyrrolizidine alkaloids, symphytine and echimidine in *Symphytum officinale* (L.) and the possibility of producing the hepatic tumours of a chronic reaction existing, it was decided that it was vitally necessary that a further investigation should be made of the alkaloids in comfrey before continuing to recommend comfrey for human or animal consumption. There is every indication that the consumption of comfrey by animals could sharply increase as an alternative source of protein in this protein-deficient world and it is being increasingly consumed by mankind because of medicinal properties. It is used in the form of fresh leaves in salads, dried leaves for tea and the root may be ground to produce a comfrey flour.

Method of Approach

Studies on the alkaloid content and toxicity were co-ordinated between the Chemistry Department of the University of Exeter, the Toxicology Unit of the Medical Research Council at Carshalton and the Michaelis Nutritional Research Laboratory at Harpenden. The studies consisted of:

1. The extraction and purification of the alkaloid for direct injection into rats to determine immediate toxicity.

2. Direct feeding experiments with rats to determine long-term chronic effects.

3. The determination of alkaloid content in the green leaves of various comfrey clones.

Comfrey root is known to have the highest concentration of alkaloid and this was used both for the source of alkaloid for injection and for the long-term feeding experiment. The alkaloid was extracted and purified in the Department of Chemistry at Exeter before being sent to the M.R.C. Toxicology Unit where the experiments with rats were conducted. The method for extraction was basically similar to that used at Harpenden for the determination of alkaloid in various comfrey clones described below.

Laboratory Technique

In order to ensure full development of the alkaloid, samples of fully grown comfrey herbage were taken from the Henry Doubleday Research Association trial ground at Bocking to the laboratory and dried at 70°C. and milled to pass through a 2mm screen. Simultaneously a determination of moisture content of the fresh material was also made.

Maximum weighed quantities of the milled leaf were extracted in a Soxhlet apparatus for 8 hours, using methanol as solvent. The methanol was then removed from the extract by carefully heating under reduced pressure on a thermomantle and the 'tarry' residue extracted with a known volume of $0.5N$ H_2SO_4. The acid extract was divided equally into two separate plastic bottles (a) and (b) and sufficient concentrated H_2SO_4. To this bottle was also added an excess of zinc powder and the contents were kept mixed with a magnetic stirrer for 3 to 4 hours, keeping the temperature below 45°C. Immediately after reduction with the zinc powder, both bottles were filtered into individual separatory funnels, rinsing the bottles and filter funnels with distilled H_2O. A few drops of phenolphthalein were added and enough concentrated NH_4OH added to turn the solution just pink—reddish brown colour. The solutions were then extracted with four small portions of $CHCl_3$ collecting the $CHCl_3$ extracts into two separate 'Quickfit' boiling tubes, any emulsions that formed being separated by passing the extract through a phase paper into the boiling tube. After the addition of enough 40 per cent NaOH to the separatory funnels to make them strongly alkaline, they were extracted with a further four small portions of $CHCl_3$ which were added to the previous $CHCl_3$ extracts in the boiling tubes.

The $CHCl_3$ extracts (a) and (b) were then individually evaporated to dryness under reduced pressure on a thermomantle, care being taken not to burn the extract by wrapping the tubes in glass wool. The extracts were redissolved in 10 ml of AR $CHCl_3$ and a suitable aliquot was pipetted into a small conical flask for titrating with 0·01M p-toluene sulphonic acid adding a speck of methyl-yellow powder to act as an indicator. A similar volume of AR $CHCl_3$ was also titrated to serve as a blank. The results were then calculated according to the formula.

$$\frac{\text{Vol. of}}{\text{titrate}} - \frac{\text{vol. of}}{\text{blank}} \times \left(2 \times \text{·0019} \times \frac{100}{\text{sample wt.}} \times \frac{\text{vol. extract}}{\text{vol. aliquot}}\right) = \frac{\text{grams \%}}{\text{alkaloid}}$$

Where the titres of the unreduced solution (a) were indicative of total tertiary bases and those of the reduced solution (b) combined tertiary bases and N-oxides representing total alkaloid.

The crude alkaloid extracts were then examined further by thin layer chromatography. Activated plates were prepared with Kielselgel G (E. Merk AG) using $CHCl_3$—MeOH—NH_4OH (85:14:1) as eluent. The chromatographed alkaloids were detected with Dragendorff's—reagent (Thies, Reuther, modified by Vagujfalvi) and intensified by subsequent spraying with ·08N H_2SO_4. The alkaloid mono-crotaline was used for a standard reference for each chromatograph and the R_F values were determined.

Results and observations

For this study the different clones of comfrey have been identified by the Bocking No. given by the Henry Doubleday Research Association at their trial ground. Description of the clones as to their habit of growth, i.e. prostrate or erect, type of leaf, colour of flow, etc., are given in Comfrey Report No. 2 (Henry Doubleday Research Association). The results are given in the following table.

TERTIARY AND TOTAL PYRROLIZIDINE ALKALOID CONTENT OF
DRIED HERBAGE OF THREE SPECIES OF COMFREY, COMFREY
MIXTURES AND SEPARATED BOCKING CLONES

Plant Material	Tertiary alkaloid per cent	Total alkaloid per cent	R_F Group
Bocking Clone			
No. 1	·024	·033	2
2	·024	·029	3
4	·015	·029	3
7	·026	·053	2
14	·022	·024	2
16	·025	·033	—
17	·011	·017	3
19	·006	·013	2
20	·014	·014	3
21	·017	·023	2
Mixed	·013	·025	—
USSR	·026	·033	—
S. officinale	·020	·034	—
S. asperum	·035	·062	1
S. Caucasicum	·024	·043	—
Tea—1	·004	·009	3
2	·010	·030	—
Monocrotaline	—	—	1
R_F Group 1	·70–·75		
,, 2	·76–·81		
,, 3	·87–·96		

Solvent: $CHCl_3 : MeOH : NH_4OH (85:14:1)$

Although differences in alkaloid content were observed between
the different clones the number of observations were too small to
establish such differences statistically. Differences were observed
between different sets of samples of the same clone and were no
doubt at least in part due to slight differences in experimental
technique involving in particular the time and temperature
involved in leaf drying and extraction. Naturally owing to the

lengthy procedure involved it was impossible to carry out the ideal
programme of processing all the samples simultaneously. This is
possibly of even greater significance than first realized as the
alkaloid proved to be unstable and was very easily oxidized and
destroyed during extraction. However it can be seen that with one
sample of comfrey tea a Tertiary alkaloid content of ·010 per cent
and a total alkaloid content of ·030 per cent was obtained which
agreed with that obtained at Exeter University and the Toxicology
Unit, whereas with another sample of comfrey tea the values were
·004 per cent and ·009 per cent respectively. At least part of this
difference may be due to differences in the plant material used for
the different tea samples and the conditions for drying the leaves.
Comfrey tea naturally is of considerable interest in this study due
to the quantities consumed for medicinal purposes by mankind and
further observations will be made on this later in the report. It
should be noted that mean values are given for two or more
different sets of samples taken at different times in the period
Sept.–Nov. Although variations were observed between samples,
no seasonal trend could be detected.

For tertiary alkaloids it is interesting to note that the lowest
concentration was observed in Bocking Clone No. 19, whereas
about six times this concentration was observed in the wild stock
S. asperum and this was also reflected in the total pyrrolizidine
alkaloid content. In general the tertiary alkaloids constituted about
50 per cent of the total value.

The variations observed in the analytical values indicated that
much larger numbers of samples and uniform conditions were
required for a comparison of the results to be statistically significant but unfortunately this could not be financially justified at this
stage. A larger number of chromatographs was also needed for the
determination of the R_F values using T.L.C. The method used is
very effective in separating out closely related alkaloid compounds
but unfortunately is less reliable in giving repetitively reproduce-
able results. In Table 1 values are given for the main spot on the
plate with a second fainter spot following fairly closely behind it.
Much more work needs to be done to sort out and identify these
chromatographic spots but this was considered to be beyond the

scope of this study. However it can be seen that with the possible exception of *S. asperum*, the alkaloids behaved quite differently from the monocrotaline standard alkaloid having higher R_F values. In their paper (1) on *S. officinale* Furuya and Araki detected symphytine and echimidine both of which they showed to be diesters having the typical nitrogenous pyrrolizidine nucleus and they found that echimidine had a lower R_F value. Thus the spots observed by us are most probably those of symphytine and echimidine or their closely related compounds. For their research the Japanese workers confined themselves to *S. asperum* only and used 5Kg (11 lb.) of root material which contained 0·226 per cent of the crude alkaloid, a massive quantity compared with the 50 gm (1·8 oz.) of dried leaf containing ·030 per cent used by us. However, our results suggest that minor differences in the alkaloid structure may well exist between the clones. Such differences could be important in terms of the stability of the alkaloids and also their toxicity.

In their paper, Furuya and Araki (1) also report on a pharmacological test with rats showing symphytine to have an LD_{50} of about 300 mg/Kg; that is an intravenous injection of 300 mg of the purified alkaloid per Kg of rat tissue caused death in approximately 50 per cent of the experimental animals. Similar experiments with alkaloid extracted from the roots of the Bocking clone No. 14 failed to demonstrate a similar toxicity at this level which may reflect slight differences in structure to which reference was previously made. For many purposes toxicity in rats is equivalent to that in mankind so that these results afford definite indication of the level of possible danger comfrey may be in human consumption. Thus in the case of comfrey tea if it be assumed that normal methods of infusion could extract just over half the alkaloid that was extracted by 8 hours in a Soxhlet apparatus in the laboratory, each cup of tea could contain 100 micrograms of alkaloid. At this level the consumer could never attain the lethal dose of 300 milligms/Kg tissue found necessary to produce the acute reaction in rats. Even to consume this quantity it would take a 150 lb. man drinking 4 cups of tea per day a total of 140 years. Furthermore it is known that to produce chronic reactions sub-lethal doses over a prolonged period are necessary. Normally such sub-lethal doses would need to be of a much higher order particularly as sensitivity to the alkaloid decreases with age.

Rats fed on a diet containing a high proportion of comfrey flour over a long period were examined after death anatomically, biochemically and histologically for symptoms of a chronic reaction of the liver to the alkaloid. Typically there is a colour reaction in the liver tissue itself, followed by the appearance of tumour cells and ultimately large visible protruding tumours. None of these symptoms were found in the experimental rats. As has been stated the alkaloid proved to be an unstable compound and was easily oxidized and it would appear conceivable that apart from its low toxivity in the purified state a considerable portion of the alkaloid would be destroyed in preparation and cooking of the comfrey flour. With fresh herbage such as leaves in salads it is possible to eat only a relatively small quantity and with its high water content the amount of alkaloid thus actually eaten by man would be very small and there would naturally be present in such herbage catalytic enzymes which would hasten its destruction. Livestock which may consume larger amounts of herbage frequently only eat it when wilted, and thus at a time when enzymatic breakdown could well have begun. Certainly prolonged and extensive use of comfrey herbage as a feeding stuff for animals has failed to reveal any deleterious effects, but rather that of considerable benefit to the health of the livestock. Furthermore it must also be remembered that many other species of plant considered safe for foodstuffs actually contain toxic alkaloids but in amounts too small to be harmful.

Conclusion

Thus from these experiments and other considerations it may be concluded that the use of comfrey as a food for mankind or animals does not present a toxic hazard from alkaloids, there being no evidence of acute or chronic hepatic reactions either to the direct injection of purified alkaloid or to prolonged consumption of comfrey root flour, which has the highest alkaloid content, by rats. From this and the much lower content of alkaloid in herbage and tea, together with the lack of any toxic evidence in livestock and the very low level of toxicity of the alkaloid itself, it may be concluded there is no toxic hazard from the use of comfrey herbage and tea.

Acknowledgements

I would like to thank Mrs. P. Walshaw of the Michaelis Nutritional Research Laboratory for her considerable help with the delicate and time-consuming processes of extraction, purification, and determination of the alkaloids and also to Dr. D. Crout of Exeter University for his personal interest and advice and also for his help in arranging the pharmacological tests with Dr. Mattocks at the M.R.C. Unit of Toxicology, and to the Henry Doubleday Research Association without whose lively co-operation this work could not have been undertaken.

References

T. Furuya and K. Araki (1968) Studies on Constituents of Crude Drugs 1 Alkaloids of *Symphytum officinale* Linn. *Chem. Pharm. Bull. 16* 2512–2516.

Appendix 2
The chemical constitution of allantoin
by Dr. A. W. Titherley, D.Sc., Ph.D., F.I.C.

In a communication to the Chemical Society in 1931,* I showed that the accepted formula for allantoin originally devised by Grimaux:

$$CO\begin{cases} NH.CO \\ \quad\quad | \\ NH.CH-NH.CO.NH_2 \end{cases}$$

will not explain all its properties, and especially its optical in-activity. Its molecule on Grimaux' formula contains an asymmetric carbon atom, namely that contained in the CH grouping, and like other compounds containing an asymmetric carbon atom, allantoin should be optically active. By this it is meant that when a ray of polarized light is passed through its solutions the plane of polariza-tion should not be undeflected as it would be with water, alcohol, etc., whose molecules are symmetrical, but rotated either to the right or left, as it is for example with the unsymmetrical molecule lactic acid, CH_3. CH. (OH) COOH.

An inspection of the latter formula shows that the central carbon atom is asymmetric, i.e. linked to four different groups, just as is the above mentioned carbon atom in the Grimaux formula. Lactic acid appears in two forms, both optically active, in opposite senses, one, d-lactic acid, rotating the plane of polarized light to the right, and the other, l-lactic acid, rotating it to the left to an exactly equal degree.

In 1913, in order to explain what appeared to be the optical abnormality of allantoin, I supposed it to be a tautomeric substance in which a double ring formula (I) alternated reversibly with that of Grimaux (II), thus:

* *Journal of the Chemical Society* Trans., ciii, 1336.

This alternation between I and II is promoted by the shift in position of one of the hydrogen atoms, believed to be mobile, a shift which by analogy with certain other types of molecule should be an easy one. Granting such a shift, involving a tautomeric change between two distinct formulae, the optical inactivity was easily explained since Formula I is strictly symmetrical, and when it changes back to Formula II, containing an asymmetric carbon atom, it must yield an equal number of molecules which are dextro-rotatory (d–) to those which are laevorotatory (l–), since there is nothing to determine a preponderance of one form; and the d–l mixture must be optically inactive by compensation, as each form must be equal and opposite in the degree of optical rotation.

Apart from the above, there were other (chemical) reasons in favour of Formula I, being at least one of the possible tautomeric forms of allantoin, though these reasons need not be considered here.

This theory of tautomerism has quite recently (1934) received indirect confirmation by the researches in France of Fosse, Thomas and Graeve (Comptes rendus, 198, 685, 1373, 1953). They have shown that it is actually possible to prepare optically active forms of allantoin if great care is exercised to prevent what is called racemization. Racemization is a well-known phenomenon in organic chemistry, viz. one by which an optically inactive mixture (equi-molecular of d– and l–) forms. Thus, suppose a given compound is wholly the d–form: on certain chemical treatment, more or less drastic, this d–form may change into the l–form, and as more and more molecules of the d–form go over the rate slows down because the reverse thing is happening (under the given treatment), with the l–molecules, and finally a state of equilibrium is attained when as many d–molecules are being regenerated from the l–molecules as are being transposed into 1–molecules. So if the process is followed by the proper optical instrument it is found that the initial dextro-rotatory compound steadily loses its activity and ends by being completely inactive, like water. It is now said to be a racemic mixture of d– and l– forms (in exactly equal amount) and the process is, as above stated, called racemization. And so it turns out that allantoin as ordinarily obtained is such a racemic mixture (or racemic compound) of the two forms, and if one of the two forms is isolated it passes with extreme ease into the racemic form, as it would be expected to do if there is an alteration between the two molecular formulae I and II.

Now it is a commonplace of Organic Chemistry that asymmetric substances found in Nature are almost invariably optically active, while the same substances produced synthetically are inactive because acemic (there being nothing to determine a preponderance of one of the forms by synthesis). It is also a well known phenomenon that when a racemic mixture is fermented by any means (say by enzymes), one of the two forms is more susceptible to decomposition than the other, which sometimes is quite unaffected. To this rule allantoin is no exception. Natural allantoin when isolated from natural sources, by carefully controlled methods to prevent racemization, is optically active as demonstrated by the above authors. It is d-allantoin and has a specific rotation for polarized light $(2) \, _D^{22} + 930$ in water, and this hitherto unknown form of allantoin has been obtained from calves urine and from certain plants, by extraction methods avoiding all rise of temperature. In all ordinary chemical properties it is identical with common allantoin, which is now recognized to be a racemic compound of d– and l– allantoin, but it might be supposed, by analogy with other optically active compounds, that there should be a biological difference between d–l–allantoin on the one hand, as well as between them and common (racemic) allantoin on the other. 1–Allantoin has been obtained by the above authors from the latter by taking advantage of selective differences in the rate of destruction at 40°C, of the two forms, by an enzyme, from soya bean, called allantoinase, the l–form preferentially surviving, as the d–allantoin ferments more rapidly.

Both d– and l– allantoin are exactly alike, except in respect of what might be termed asymmetric properties such as optical activity, where they are opposite and equal. Each on warming in solution passes over into the racemic form, common allantoin.

It is well known that many of the bio-chemical manifestations of living matter are concerned with the transformation (such as oxidation, reduction, hydrolysis, etc.) of complex asymmetric compounds, proteins, carbohydrates, phosphatides and so on, most of which display optical activity and are therefore not racemic forms. Indeed chemical asymmetry plays a fundamental role in life, as is well known from numerous cases which have been established, and probably allantoin is no exception to this. It is apparently the unstable d–form which, so far as is known, normally functions in the living plant and animal. When therefore ordinary racemix (d–l) allantoin is applied therapeutically it may be presumed provisionally that only one half of it (d–) is active and the other half (l–) is inert, but as yet nothing definite is known about this. In any case when ordinary allantoin is brought into solution by heating with water it no doubt passes partly into the symmetrical double-ring form l (p. 240) and even with cold water it is probable that a small quantity of I co-exists in solution with the asymmetric form II, and the equilibrium between these two forms, I and II, will be disturbed by numerous chemical agencies. For instance, the influence of acids and alkalis would be expected to be profound and thus the pH value of the solution, as representing the concentration of hydrogen (oxonium) ions will be a determining factor in this equilibrium. As is well known with pH7, as it is in the purest distilled water, we have absolute neutrality, meaning a very small but definite value for hydrogen-ion concentration. With small quantities of alkali present (even as dissolved out of glass when boiled with water) the pH rises, and when at a value of say 8 or 9 there is a marked alkalinity. On a priori grounds this should favour a more rapid establishment of equilibrium between forms I and II and also a preponderance of the asymmetrical form II, because this is the more acidic of the two forms. Allantoin belongs to a group of chemical substances known as amphoteric, because they function as weak acids in their behaviour towards alkalis, forming alkali salts, and as weak bases towards acids, forming salts with such acids. Allantoin, for example, yields a well-defined crystalline nitrate with nitric acid and it dissolves in caustic soda much more readily than it does in water because it forms a sodium salt (very unstable). It is also important to observe that allantoin as an acid is considerably stronger in hot aqueous solutions than it is in cold. When its aqueous solution is acid for any reason (say on heating or when acid is definitely added) the hydrogen-ion concentration increases. This, as in the case of alkali-effect, will promote a more rapid attainment of equilibrium between forms I and II, but for certain chemical reasons it is likely that it favours the predominance of the symmetrical form I.

We may sum up, then, by saying that allantoin will be very sensitive to acidity and alkalinity, as well as to high temperature, but that there is reason now (after the work of Fosse, Thomas, and Graeve) to believe that the predominating form in neutral solution (pH $= 7$) in the cold is the asymmetrical form II.

Apart from these considerations, affecting only the reversible equilibrium between form I and the two optically active forms (d– and l–) of II and readily accounting for the easy racemization of the latter, it must be noted that allantoin is a chemically unstable substance, readily converted by various chemical agencies into the other chemical compound related to it, but in no way identical with it. The most striking of these changes is that observed with strong alkaline solutions. Here the first stage is its conversion into the salt already referred to, but on standing in the cold this salt decomposes by rupture of the ring in Formula II yielding the salt of a definite acid, called allantoic acid, which is itself very unstable and may be converted into a number of derivatives, these being as yet but imperfectly understood. It is quite possible that some of these derivatives appear in animal and vegetable life but have not been identified owing to their very soluble, syrupy and non-crystallizable nature.

Index